# IMA! 2

## Workbook

**Sue Burnham**

Photography by Michael Sedunary
Illustrated by Roger Harvey

なまえ: ______________________ くみ: ________

せんせいのなまえ: ______________________

EMCParadigm

Edited by Tina Hutchings
Proofread by Atsushi Takagi
Designed by Tanya Lea with assistance from Fabrice Rocher and Aisling Gallagher
Consultant: Yuki Itani
Handwritten kanji and illustrations on p 55, p 77, p 84 (heart), p 112, p 113, p 126, p 170 and p 179 (top pic) by Kae Sato-Goodsell
Map on p 144 by Guy Holt
Production by Michelle Sweeney

First published by CIS•Heinemann
Australia

ISBN 978-0-8219-2368-9
ISBN 0-8219-2368-4



**Published by EMC/Paradigm Publishing**
875 Montreal Way
St. Paul, Minnesota 55102
800-328-1452
www.emcp.com
E-mail: educate@emcp.com

Printed in China by W K T
3 4 5 6 7 8 9 10 XXX 08 07 06

**Acknowledgements**

**Photography**
p 42 (pic 5) by Soepri Soehodo
p 43 (pic 4) supplied by Jason Worthy

The publishers wish to thank the following companies and institutions who kindly gave permission to reproduce copyright material in this book:
p 3 Canada travel brochure. Permission by Play Guide Tour
pp 4, 90 Wraps. Permission by Japan Subway
p 25 Game boy. Permission by Nintendo Australia Pty Ltd
p 75 Man on mobile phone. Permission by NTT DoCoMo
pp 89, 95 Drinks. Permission by Doutour
p 95 Healthy drinks. Permission by Mister Donut
pp 27, 89, 95, 97 Fries, burger, thick shake, apple pie, ice cream Permission by McDonald's Japan

# もくじ

## カタカナ



## 第一課



## 第二課



## 第三課



## 第四課

# カタカナ

**1** Here are some examples of advertisements. Use three different colored highlighters or pencils to show that you can recognize ひらがな, かんじ and カタカナ.
You could use the カタカナ table from 3 ページ of your textbook to try to work out some of the カタカナ words to find out what is being advertised.

2 These カタカナ letters are said to look like their ひらがな equivalents. See if you agree by writing the ひらがな letter in the small box provided.

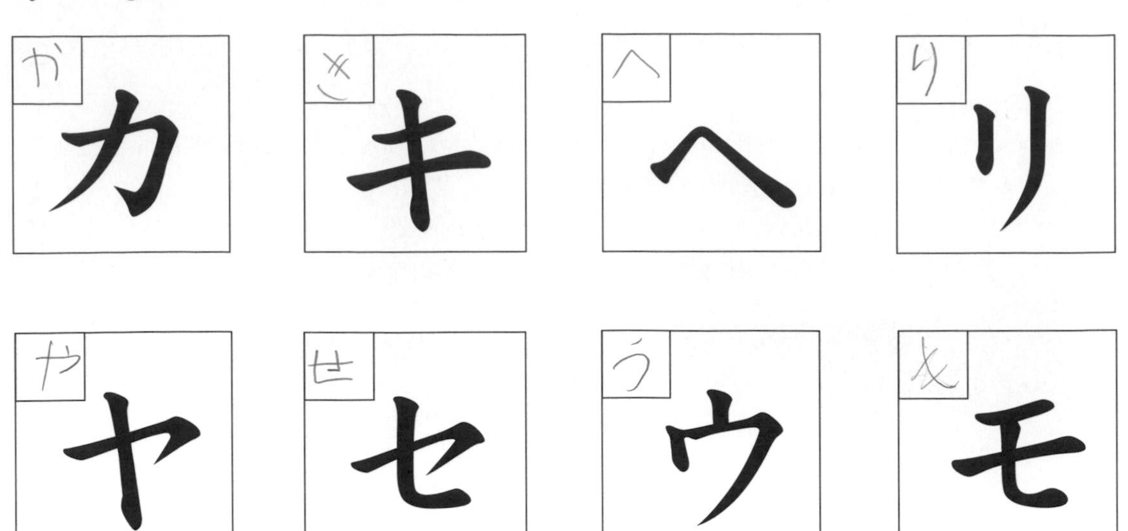


3 Practice writing these katakana letters.

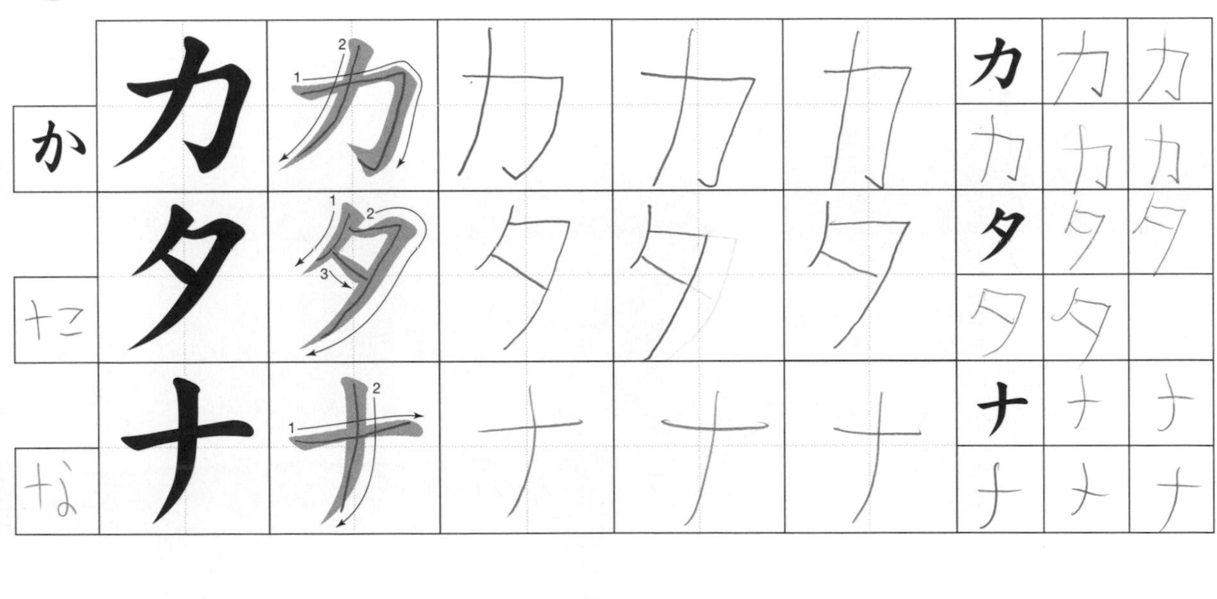


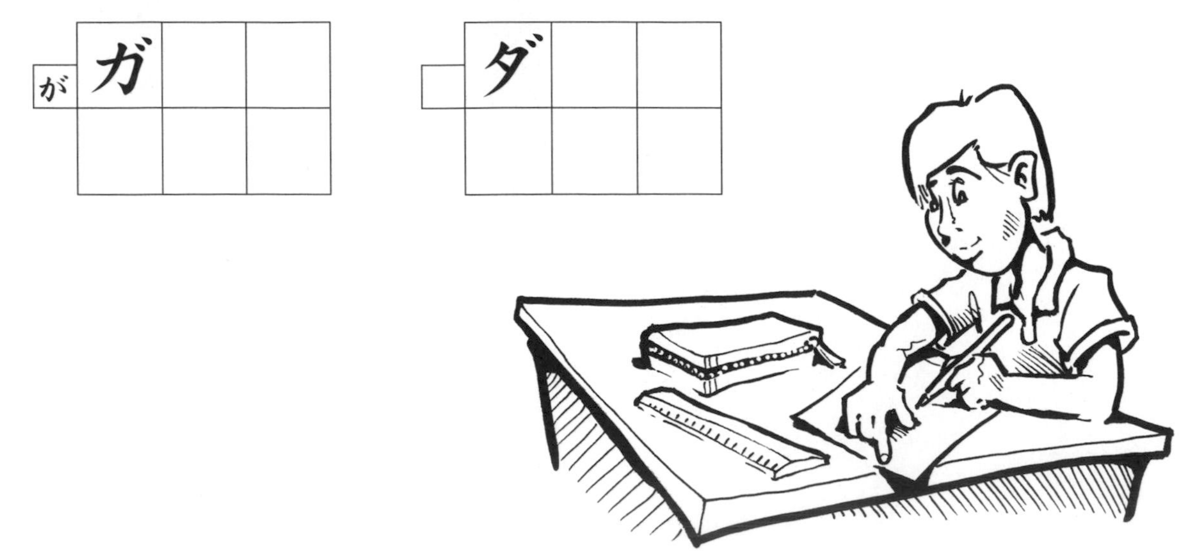

**4** This is a travel brochure advertising Canada as a vacation destination. However, 'Canada' has been left off. Write it in the empty space using カタカナ.

**5** Complete these カタカナ words and then draw a line to match the word to an appropriate picture.

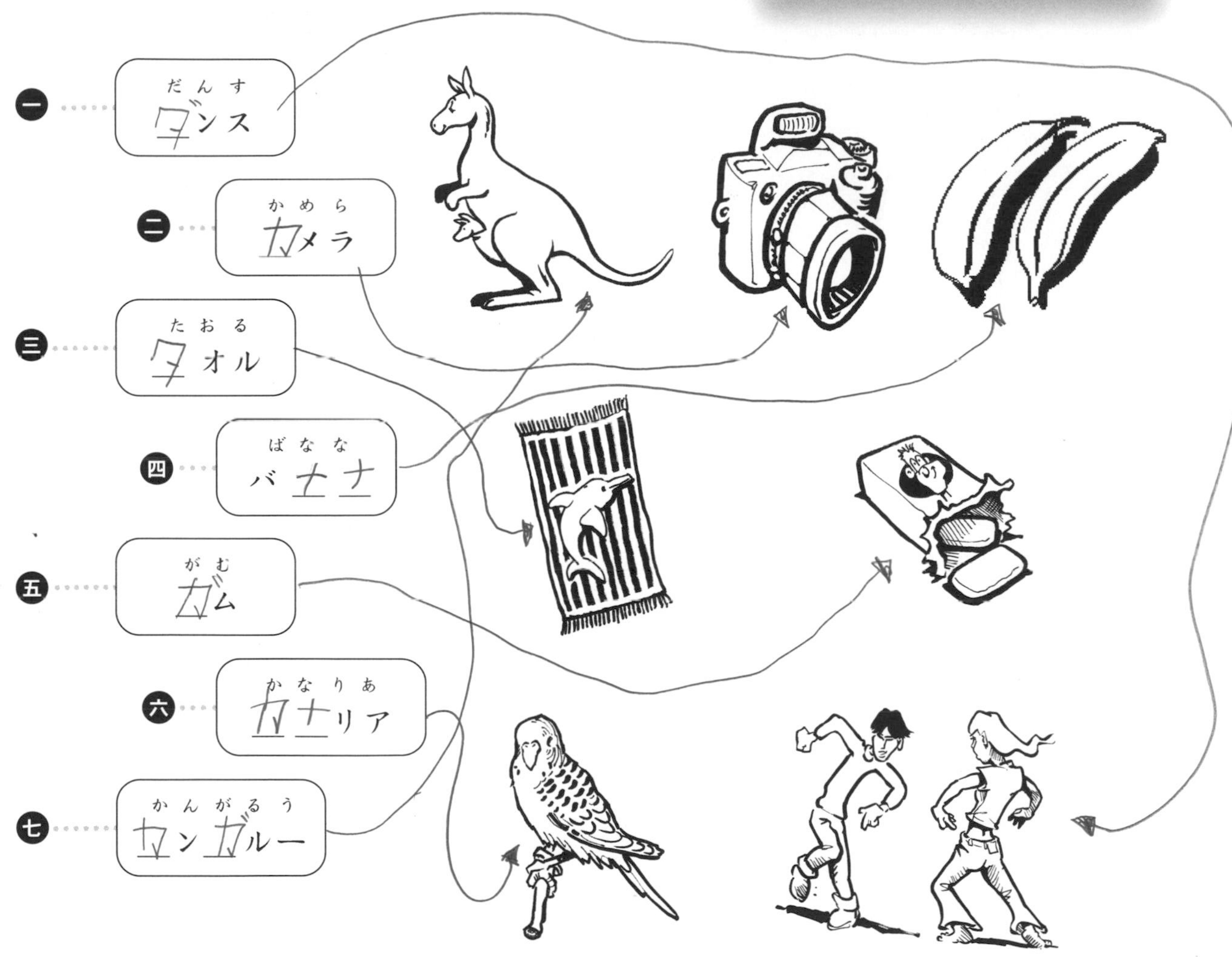


**6** Fill in the カタカナ letters that you now know on the blank tables which are on the inside covers of this workbook.

| カ | ガ | タ | ダ | ナ |
|---|---|---|---|---|

# カタカナ1

❶ Draw a line to match these food items with their correct label.

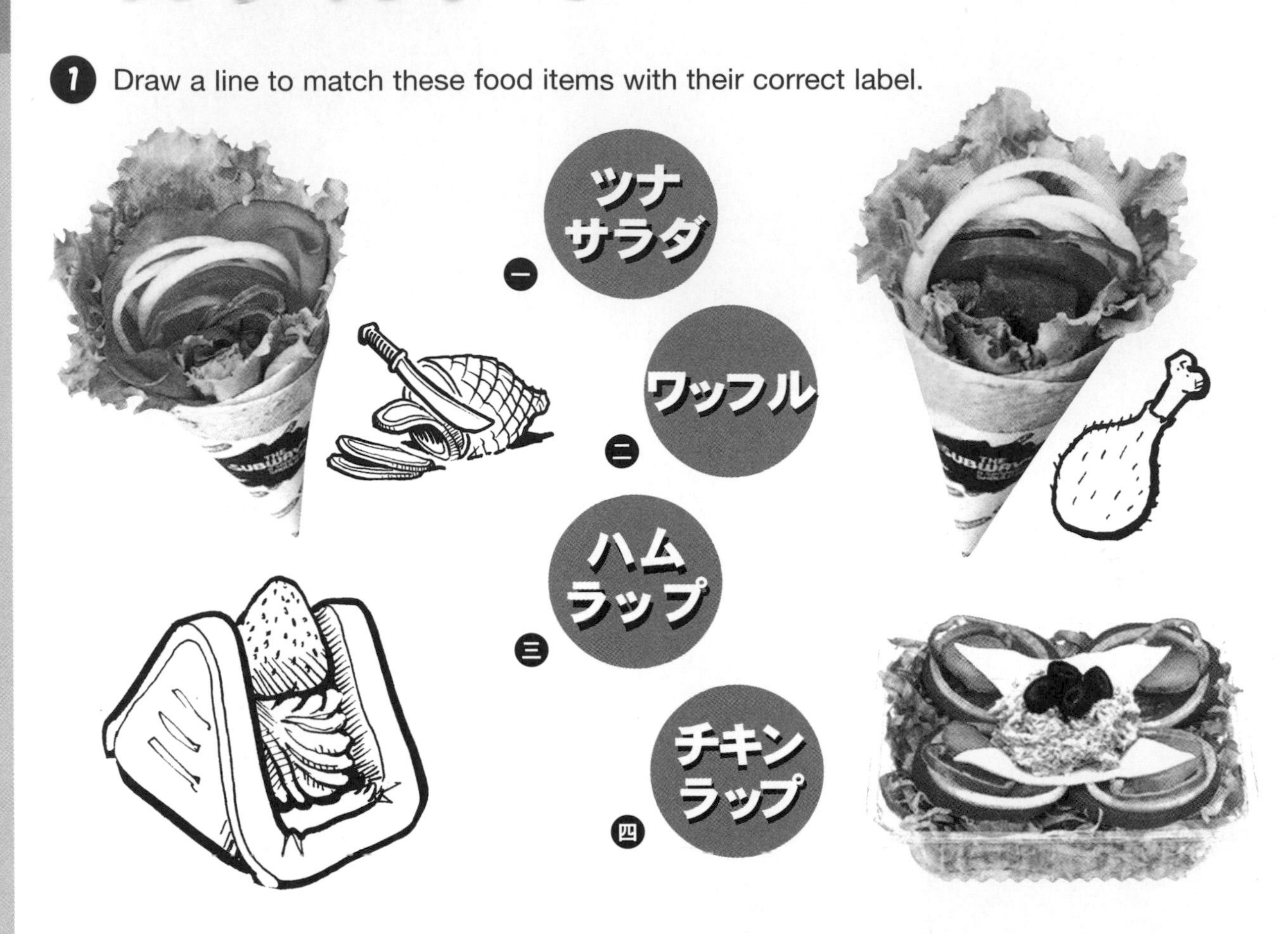


❷ Practice writing these カタカナ letters.

| | | | | | | | |
|---|---|---|---|---|---|---|---|
| キ | キ | | | | キ | | |
| サ | サ | | | | サ | | |
| チ | チ | | | | チ | | |
| ツ | ツ | | | | ツ | | |

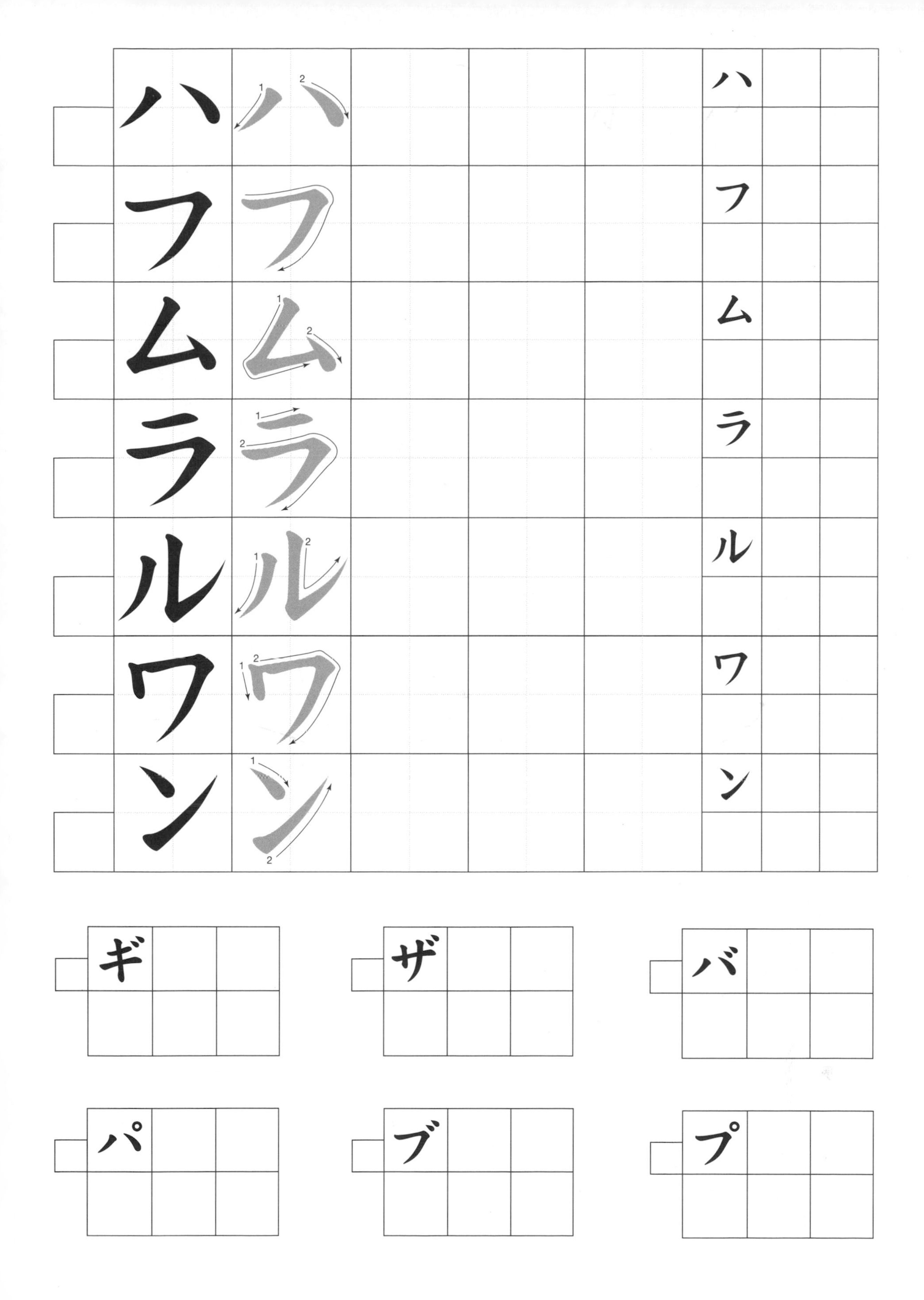
ハ
フ
ム
ラ
ル
ワ
ン
ギ
ザ
バ
パ
ブ
プ

**3** Choose the word that best fits the description and write it in the space provided.

**1** Which is *not* a musical instrument?

ギター　　ハープ　　パンダ　　ドラム　　________________

**2** Which is *not* something you wear?

パーカー　　パンツ　　サンダル　　プール　　________________

**3** Which can you eat?

パンチ　　ランチ　　キッチン　　ハンカチ　　________________

**4** Which is *not* connected with tennis?

サーバー　　ラブ　　サーブ　　サッカー　　________________

**5** Which is *not* a meat?

ハム　　ラム　　ツナ　　チキン　　________________

**6** Which does *not* apply to your favorite male sports star?

パワフル　　ラッキー　　タフ　　ハンサム　　________________

**4** きいてみよう

Listen as these people talk about their hunger pangs! Write the number of the conversation under the picture showing what they decide to have.

一

二

三

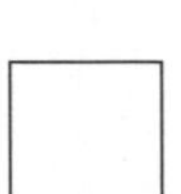

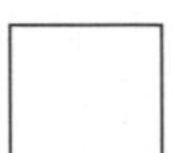

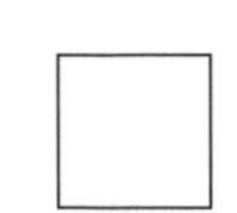

四

五

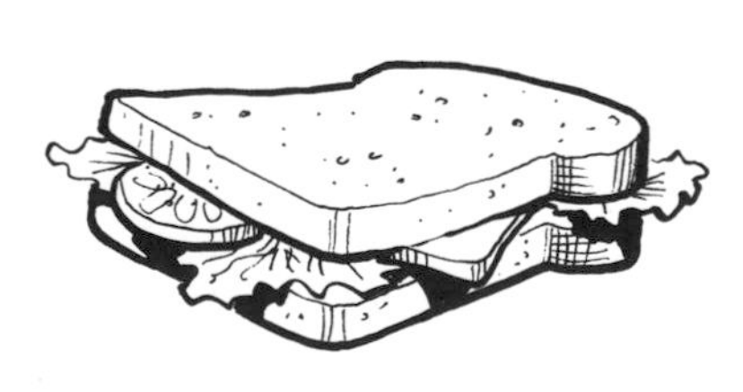

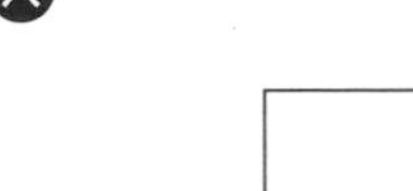

六

**5** Change these 〜ます verbs to suggestions using 〜ましょう. Then write the suggestion in English. The first has been done for you.

| | | | |
|---|---|---|---|
| 1 | たべます | たべましょう | let's eat |
| 2 | のみます | | |
| 3 | 見ます | | |
| 4 | とります | | |
| 5 | つくります | | |
| 6 | します | | |
| 7 | ききます | | |
| 8 | がんばります | | |
| 9 | あそびます | | |
| 10 | 行きます | | |
| 11 | よみます | | |
| 12 | かいます | | |
| 13 | かえります | | |
| 14 | おわります | | |

**6** Complete these sentences with a suggestion. The first has been done for you.

1 ギターをれんしゅう しましょう＿＿＿＿＿＿。

2 CDを＿＿＿＿＿＿。

3 ワッパ ーバーガーを＿＿＿＿＿＿。

4 かいものに＿＿＿＿＿＿。

5 おもしろいえいがを＿＿＿＿＿＿。

6 カタカナを＿＿＿＿＿＿。

7 カプチーノ(の)を＿＿＿＿＿＿。

**7** Write these sentences using かんじ, ひらがな and カタカナ.

1 Let's go to Sam's house.

______________________________

2 How about having a ham and chicken wrap?
Sounds good.

______________________________

______________________________

3 Shall I buy some bread and butter?

______________________________

4 Let's watch the soccer.

______________________________

**8** Write labels for these items.

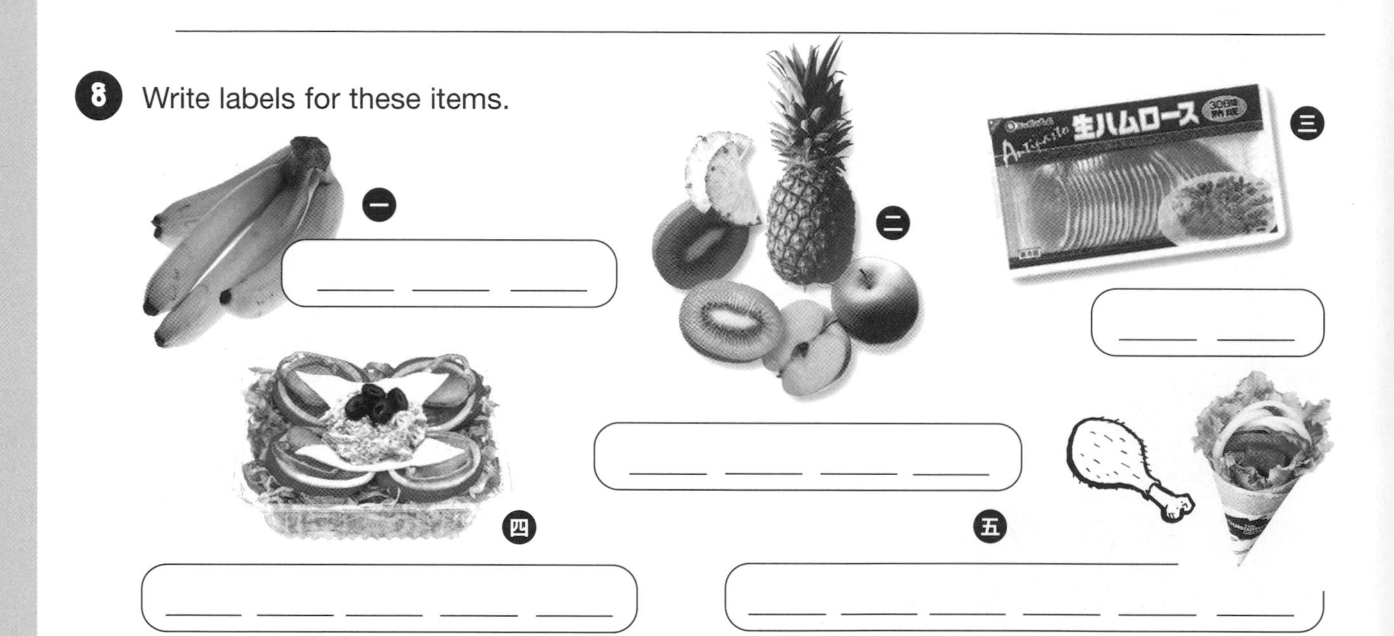


**9** Write the clues in English for this puzzle, which contains the names of different countries.

| | | | | | | |
|---|---|---|---|---|---|---|
| | | | | 1 フ | | |
| | | | 2 ブ | ラ | ジ(じ) | 3 ル |
| | | | | ン | ■ | ワ |
| | | 4 パ | キ | ス(す) | タ | ン |
| 5 ガ | ー | ナ | | | | ダ |
| | | マ(ま) | | | | |

➢ よこ

2 ______________________

4 ______________________

5 ______________________

∀ たて

1 ______________________

3 ______________________

4 ______________________

**10** Fill in the カタカナ letters that you now know on the blank tables on the inside covers of this workbook.

キ ギ サ ザ チ ツ ハ バ パ フ ブ プ ム ラ ル ワ ン

# カタカナ2

**1** Write the number of the picture next to its correct label.

- ローラーブレード ☐
- トレーニング ☐
- トランプ ☐
- スカイ ダイビング ☐
- ピクニック ☐
- ダンス ☐

**2** Practice writing these カタカナ letters.

| | | | | | | | |
|---|---|---|---|---|---|---|---|
| イ | イ | | | | イ | | |
| ク | ク | | | | ク | | |
| ス | ス | | | | ス | | |
| ト | ト | | | | ト | | |
| ニ | ニ | | | | ニ | | |
| ヒ | ヒ | | | | ヒ | | |
| ヘ | ヘ | | | | ヘ | | |
| マ | マ | | | | マ | | |
| レ | レ | | | | レ | | |
| ロ | ロ | | | | ロ | | |

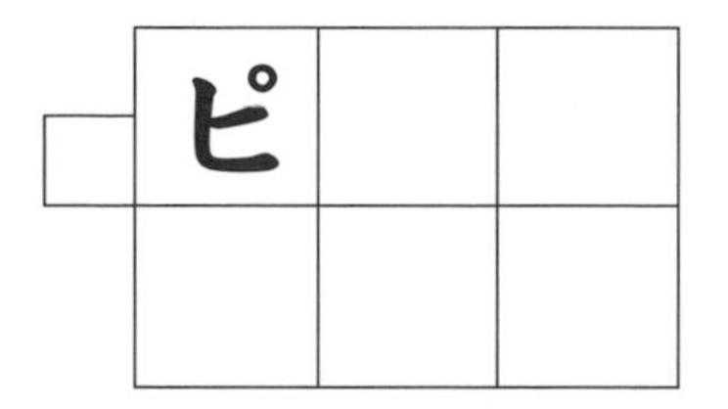


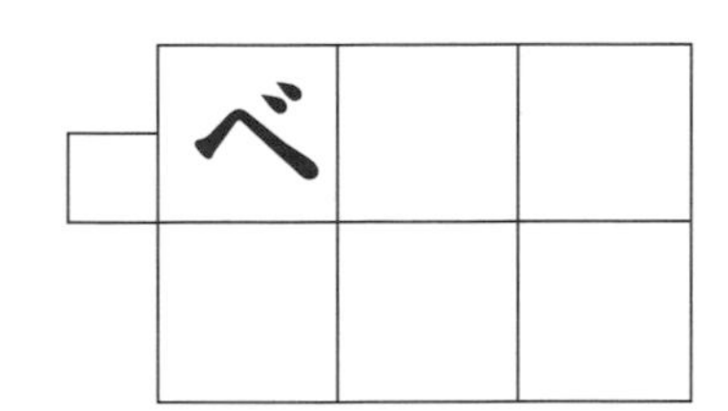


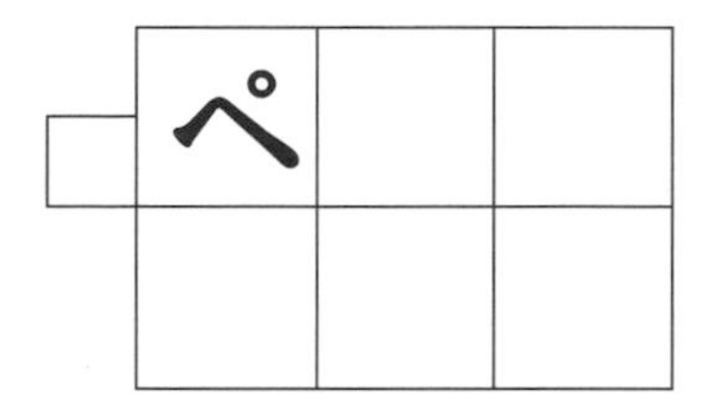


**3** What do you like? Write these words in the order of things you like most to things you like least.

**1** On your トースト

マーマレード　チーズ
ピーナツバター

______________________

______________________

______________________

**2** As a snack

ドーナツ　クッキー　スープ

______________________

______________________

______________________

**3** For lunch

パイ　サンドイッチ　ピザ

______________________

______________________

______________________

**4** As a hero（ヒーロー）

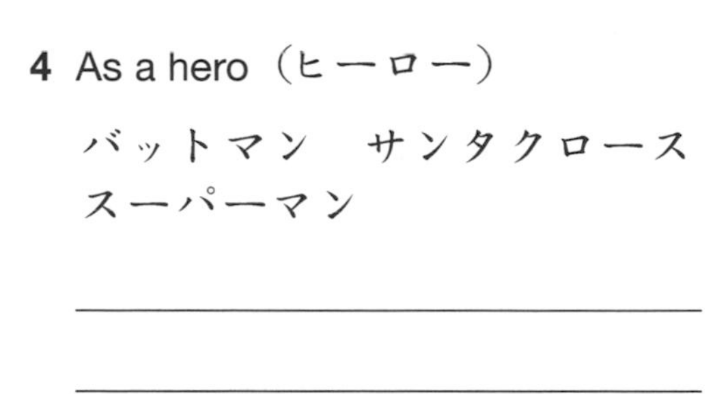

バットマン　サンタクロース
スーパーマン

______________________

______________________

______________________

**5** As a sport

ダイビング　スキー　ハイキング

______________________

______________________

______________________

## ❹ きいてみよう

Listen as these people talk about the weekend. Write the number in the box of the picture that best represents their conversation.

**5** Look at this medley race. What stroke is each competitor swimming?
Choose from the words below and write your answer in the space under each competitor.

| フリースタイル　バックストローク　バタフライ |
|---|

____________________　____________________　____________________

**6** Complete these sentences using words from the box below.

| パイナップル　ロマンチック　ピクニック　カレンダー　ロックンロール |
|---|

**1** きのうこうえんで ________________ をしました。たのしかったです。

**2** わたしはフルーツが大すきです。このおいしい ________________

をたべましょうか。

**3** いちばんすきなおんがくは ________________ です。

**4** これはラブレターです。ぼくのガールフレンドは

とても ________________ です。

**5** 今日は13日ですよ。________________ を見て！

**7** Draw pictures of the following things.

1 サングラス

2 ベッド

3 ワークブック

4 マッチ

5 クロスワード パズル

6 ハンドバッグ

7 レタス

8 トイレットペーパー

**8** Fill in the カタカナ letters that you now know on the inside covers.

イ　ク　グ　ス　ズ　ト　ド　ニ　ヒ　ビ　ピ　ヘ　ベ　ペ　マ　レ　ロ

# カタカナ3

**1** Write the number of the label under the correct picture.

一 

二 

三 

四 カヌー

五 ミニカー

六 

**2** Practice writing these カタカナ letters.

オ オ オ

ケ ケ ケ

シ シ シ

ヌ ヌ ヌ

ノ ノ ノ

ホ ホ ホ

ミ ミ ミ

モ モ モ

ヨ ヨ ヨ

ゲ ジ ボ ポ

**3** Draw a line to connect each word to the matching item in the illustrations below.

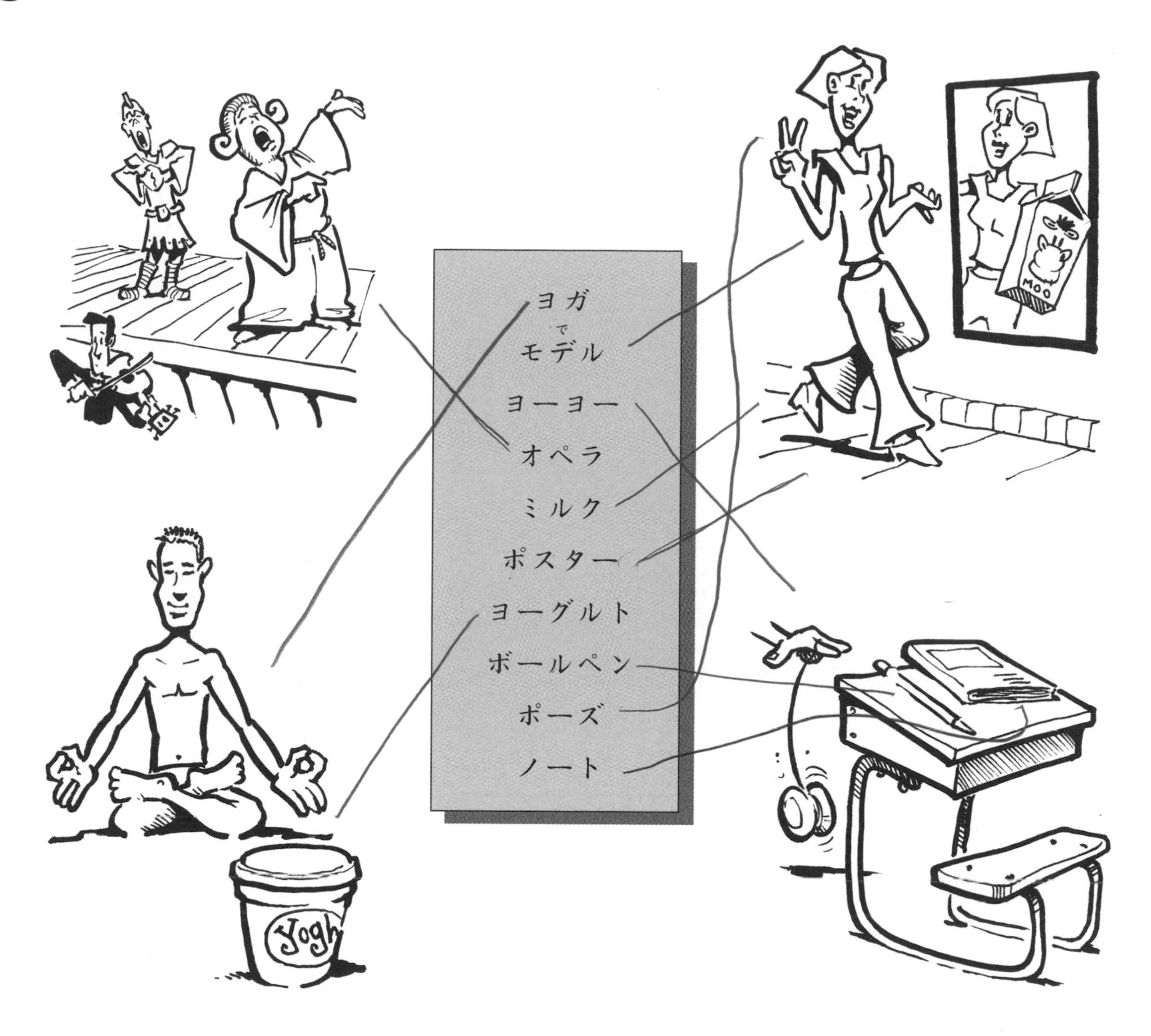


**4** Write the word you think that does not belong in each of these lists.

**1** ホットドッグ　　オムレツ　　シーフードサラダ　　ローストビーフ

______________________________

**2** ケーキ　　ヌガー　　ペパーミント　　ガム

______________________________

**3** バドミントン　　ロッククライミング　　ボクシング

______________________________

**4** オレンジ　　グレープフルーツ　　パイナップル　　レモン

______________________________

5 Can you work out the meanings of these オール, マイ, カー and ミニ words? Write your answer next to each word. After you have worked out the meanings of the words, write labels for the illustrations.

オール

オールナイト ______

オールスターチーム ______

オールスター ______

マイ

マイペース ______

マイカー ______

マイホーム ______

カー

スポーツカー ______

オープンカー ______

レンタカー ______

ミニ

ミニカー ______

ミニスカート ______

ミニパトロールカー ______
（ミニパト）

## 6 きいてみよう

For each conversation, circle the picture that best represents what they decide to do.

Conversation 一

Conversation 二

Conversation 三

Conversation 四

Conversation 五

**7** These words all contain little ッ. Add little ッ and work out the meaning of the word. A scrambled list of the English words is given below – refer to this after you have had a go at working out the English yourself.

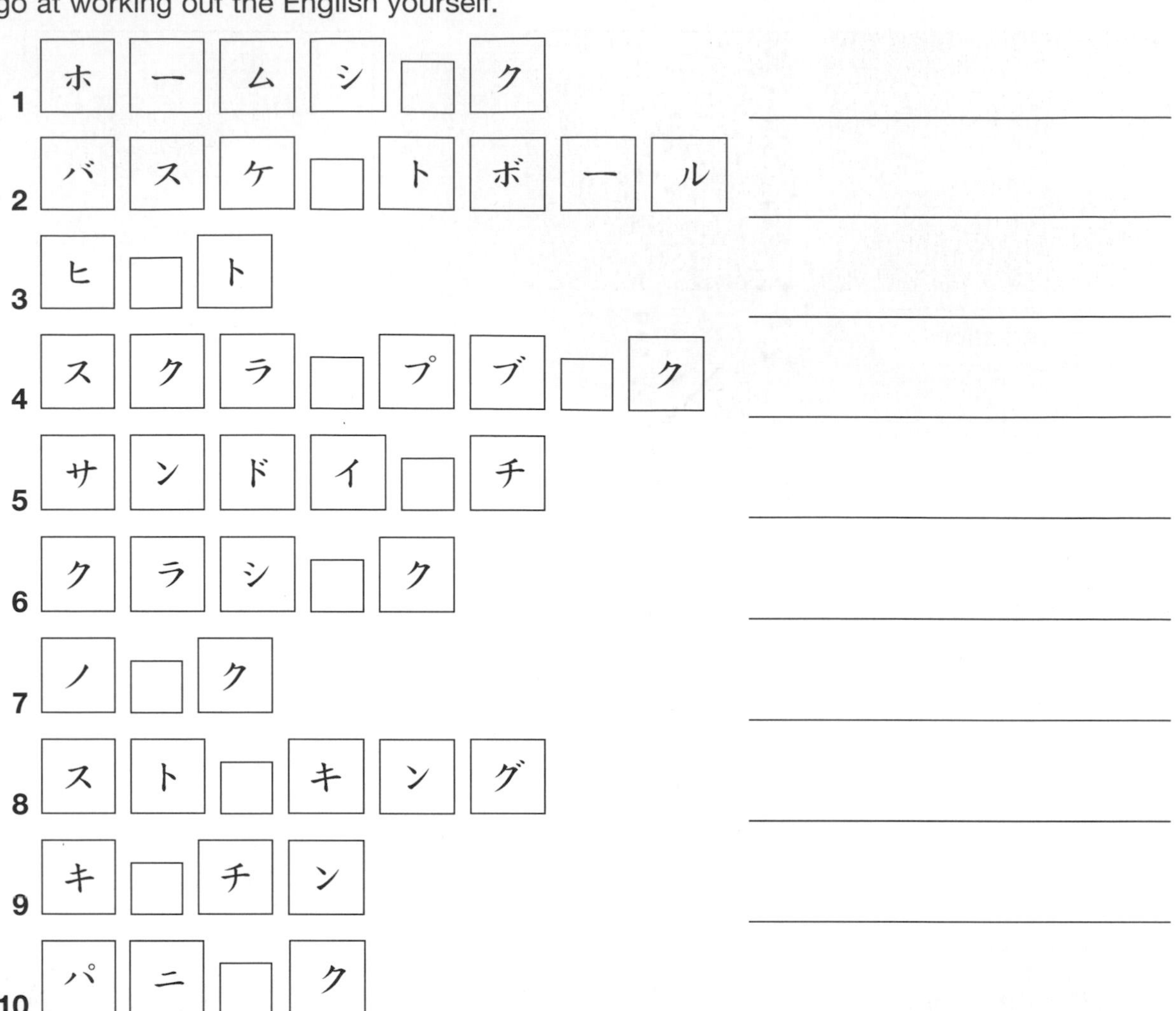


| | | | | |
|---|---|---|---|---|
| scrapbook | homesick | kitchen | panic | hit |
| sandwich | classic | stocking | basketball | knock |

**8** Here are some English expressions that are used in Japanese. Try to identify them.

1 グッド・タイミング ______________________

2 オーケー ______________________

3 ノー・プロブレム ______________________

4 グッド・ラック ______________________

**9** Fill in the カタカナ letters that you now know on the inside covers.

オ ケ ゲ シ ジ ヌ ノ ホ ボ ポ ミ モ ヨ

# カタカナ４

**1** Draw a line to match each item with the correct label.

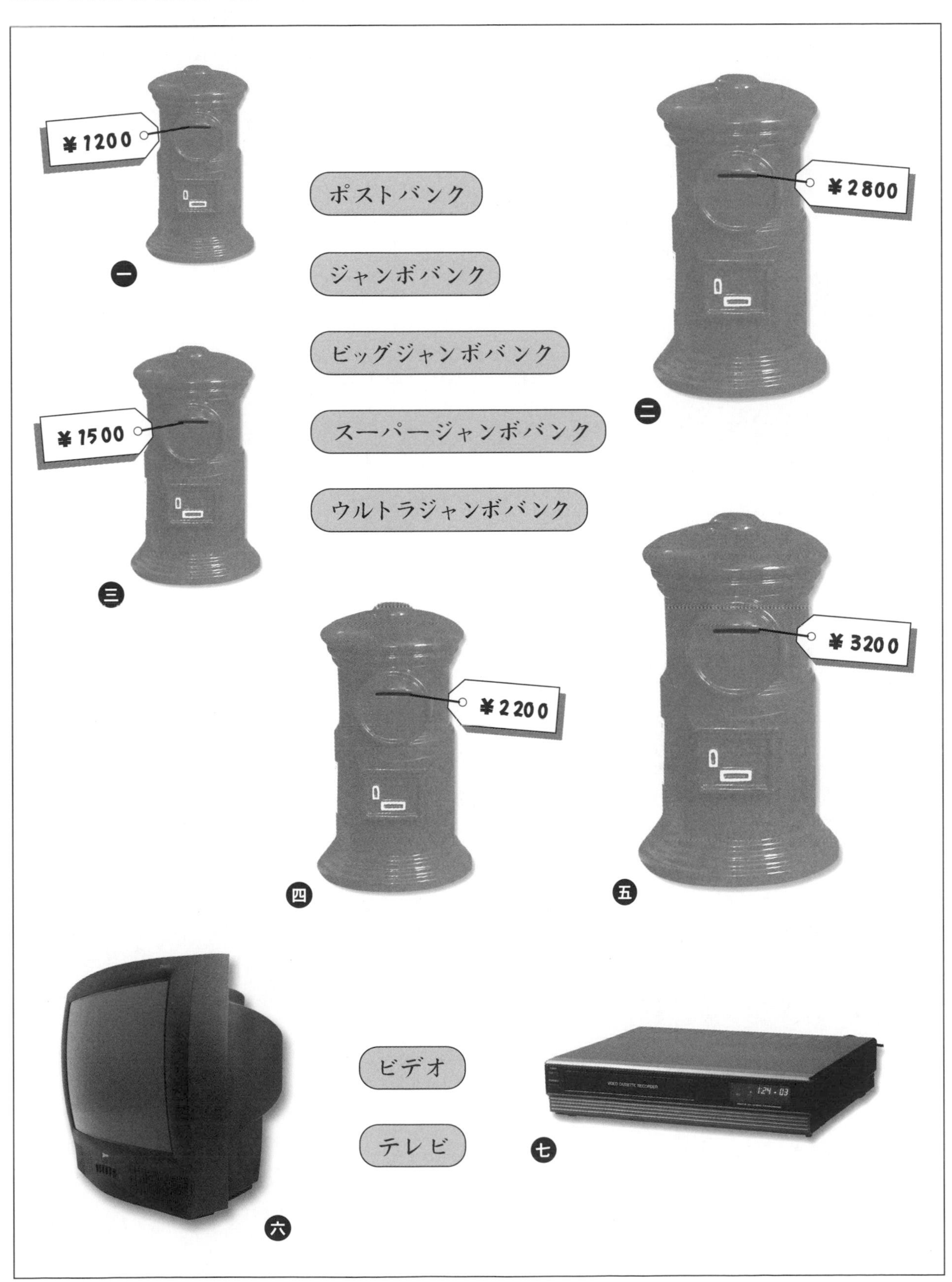

**2** Practice writing these カタカナ letters.

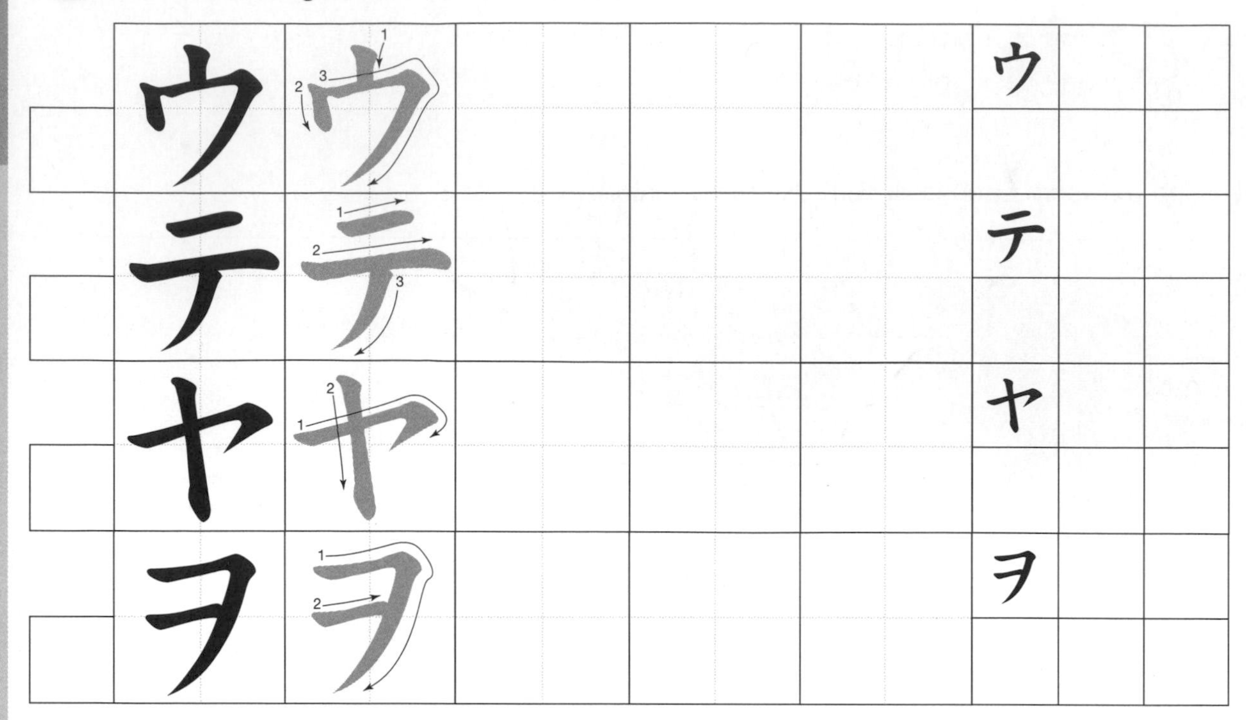

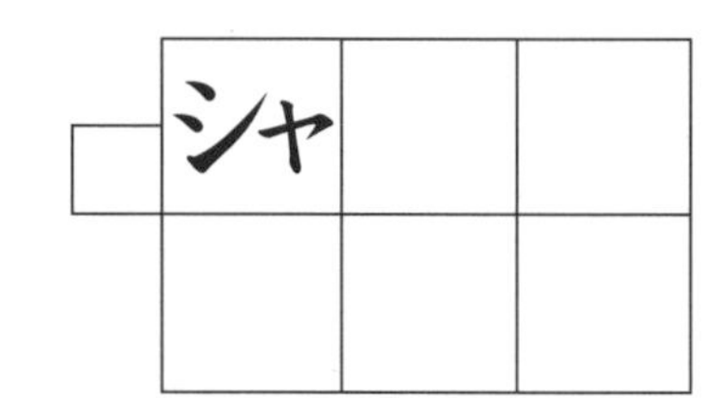

**3** **1** Circle which of the following items you have.

ステレオ　　テレビ　　ビデオ　　CDプレーヤー　　ビデオゲーム

**2** Circle which of the following are African countries.

ウガンダ　　ルワンダ　　デンマーク　　モザンビーク

**3** Circle which of the following are European countries.

スペイン　　シンガポール　　ベトナム　　フランス　　ペルー

**4** Circle which of the following are things you can eat.

ジャム　　シャンプー　　ジャズ　　シャーベット

## 4 きいてみようA

Listen as the owner of this fruit stand encourages the customers to buy his fruit. Write down the prices of the fruit as he gives them.

| | | | | | |
|---|---|---|---|---|---|
| | | | | | |

## 5 きいてみようB

These students are being interviewed about their monthly おこづかい, or pocket money. This could be useful information for you in attempts to get yours increased!
Write down the amount that each one receives next to their name on the list below.

**1** えつ子 ¥________ **2** ひろまさ ¥________

**3** じゅん子 ¥________ **4** ともあき ¥________

**5** まり子 ¥________ **6** おさむ ¥________

## 6 きいてみようC

ビンゴ！Choose and write down five numbers between (and including) those given in the first column. When you hear a number that you have written down, cross it out. When you have crossed out all five numbers call out ビンゴ！

In the スコア column, enter how many numbers you were able to cross out for each game. The person with the highest final total will be the チャンピオン!

| | | | | | | | スコア |
|---|---|---|---|---|---|---|---|
| **1** | 100→900 (in 100s) | | | | | | /5 |
| **2** | 1000→9000 (in 1000s) | | | | | | /5 |
| **3** | 10 000→100 000 (in 10 000s) | | | | | | /5 |
| | | | | | | トータル | |

7 They're having a sale at the sports shop and your job is to prepare the labels for the goods. You have been given a master list to work from and you are required to write the name of the item on the appropriate label.

スキー　スノーボード　バスケットボールのフープ
ホッケーのスティック　サッカーのシャツ　テニスラケット
テニスボール　ローラーブレード　Tシャツ

一
______
______
¥______

二
______
______
¥______

三
______
______
¥______

四
______
______
¥______

五
______
______
¥______

六
______
______
¥______
______
______
¥______

七
______
______
¥______

八
______
______
¥______

8 きいてみようD

Now the manager at the sports shop wants you to write in the sale prices. Listen as she tells you what they are and write them in the spaces above.

**9** Write labels for the following things.

一

二

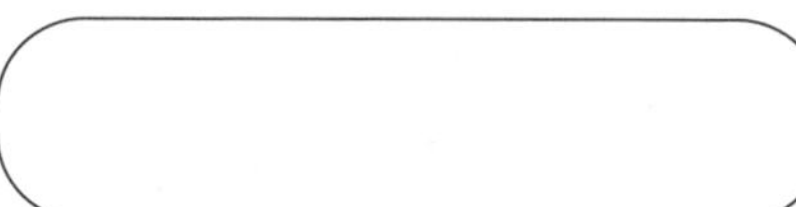

三

四

五

六

**10** Fill in the カタカナ letters that you now know on the inside covers.

ウ テ デ ヤ ヲ

# カタカナ5

**1** Write the number of each menu item next to its label.

**2** Practice writing these カタカナ letters.

| | | | |
|---|---|---|---|
| あ | ア | ア (1, 2) | ア |
| え | エ | エ (1, 2, 3) | エ |
| こ | コ | コ (1, 2) | コ |
| せ | セ | セ (1, 2) | セ |

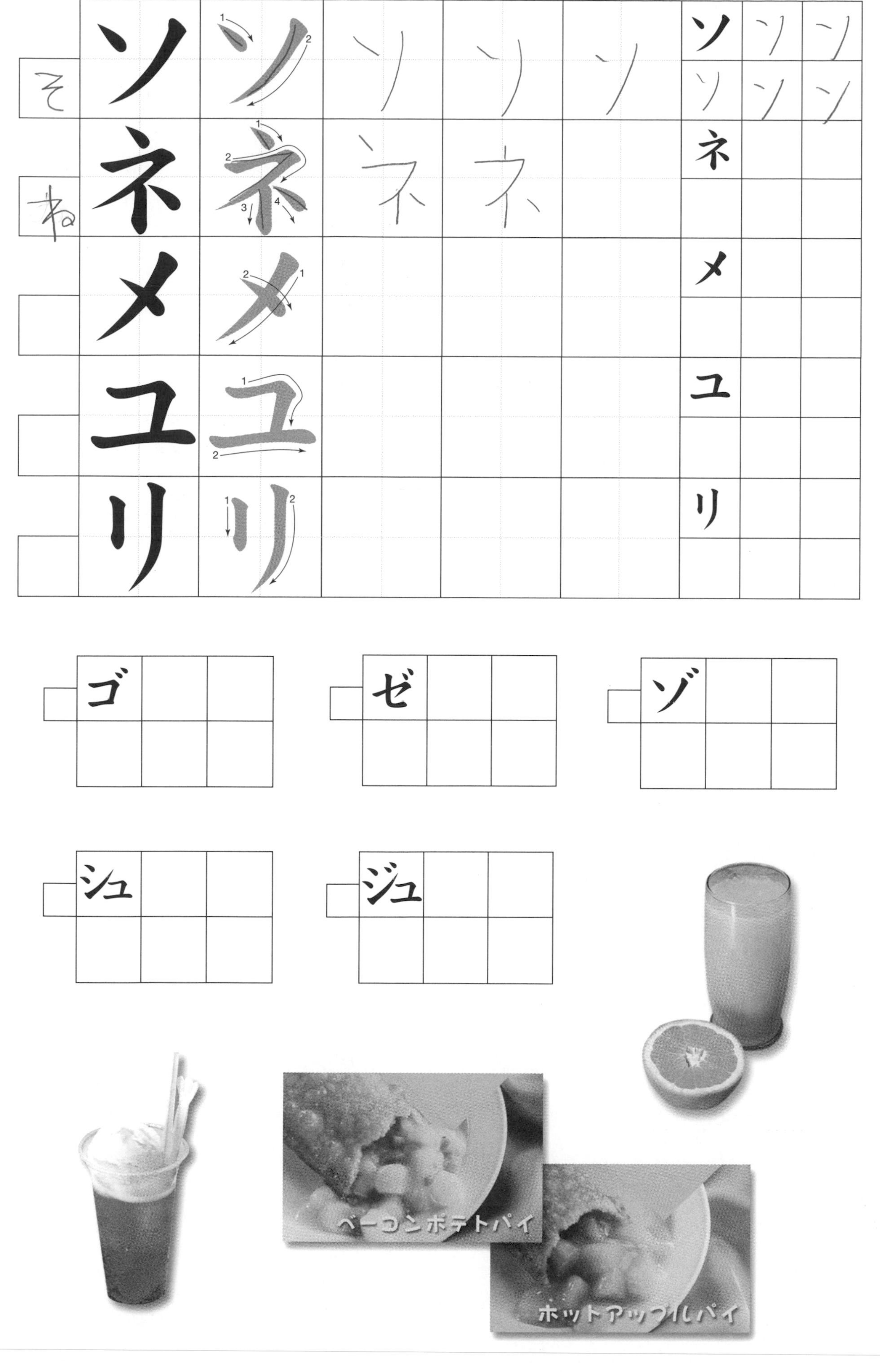
ソ
ネ
メ
ユ
リ
ゴ
ゼ
ゾ
シュ
ジュ
ベーコンポテトパイ
ホットアップルパイ

**3** Many famous Japanese company names are written in カタカナ. Complete this list of names and カタカナ.
What are some of the products that these companies are famous for? Draw a line to match the name to a product.

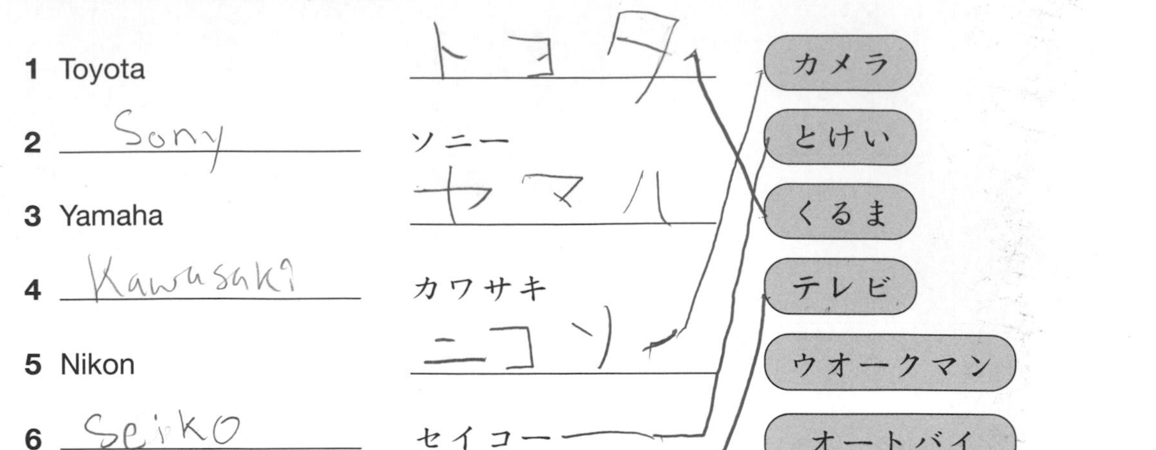

1 Toyota ______

2 ______ ソニー

3 Yamaha ______

4 ______ カワサキ

5 Nikon ______

6 ______ セイコー

7 Sharp ______



**4** These people are モデル for various kinds of ウエア. Choose from the box below and write a label for each person to describe what they are wearing.

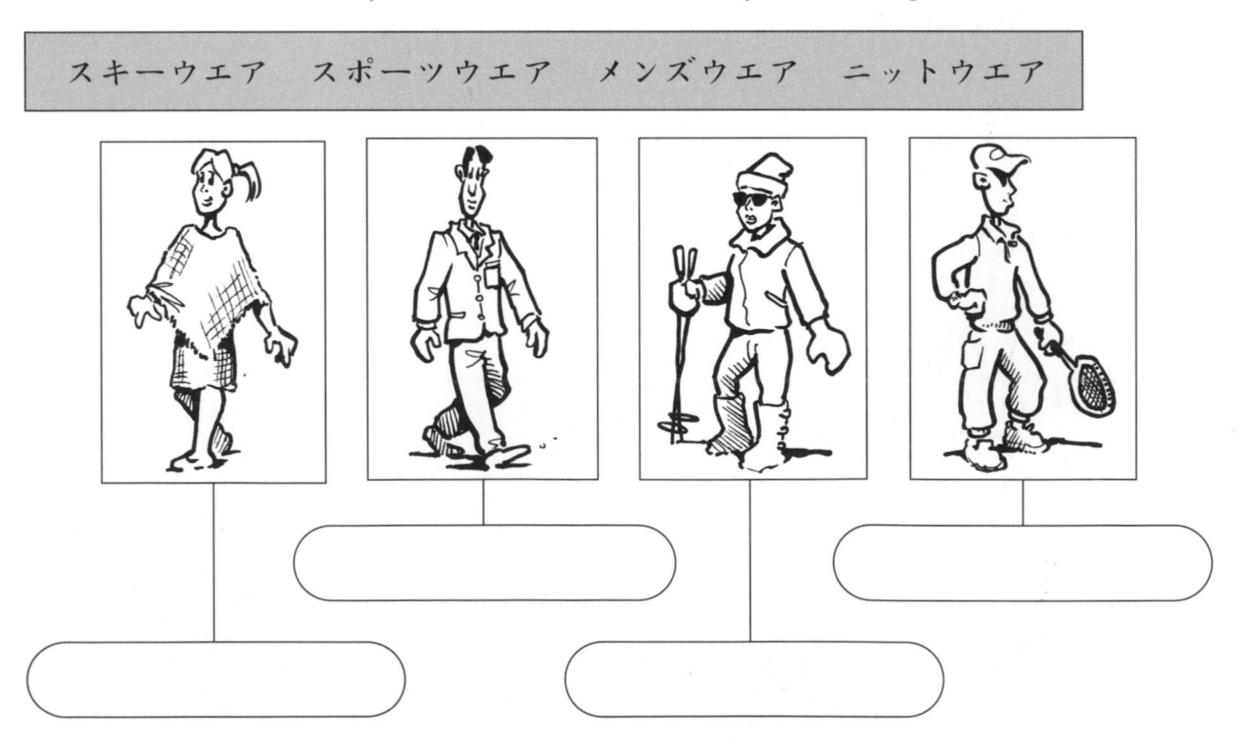



**5** Can you suggest where you might see or hear these アウト words?

1 ノックアウト ______

2 アウトバック ______

3 アウトドアライフ ______

**6** Some Japanese loan words are difficult to recognize because of the way in which they have become shortened. Try to guess the meanings of these words. (The full words are given below.)

1 パソコン Personal Computer
2 アメフト American Football
3 アニメ Anime, Animation
4 リモコン Remote Control
5 スーパー Super market
6 コンビニ Convienent Store

| パーソナル・コンピューター　アメリカン・フットボール　アニメーション<br>リモート・コントロール　スーパー・マーケット　コンビニエンス・ストア |
|---|

**7** Many Japanese use the following English expressions. Try to work them out – saying them out loud in Japanese may help.
(Sometimes a dot is used to separate expressions that have more than one word.)

1 グッド・アイディア ________
2 ネバー・ギブ・アップ！ ________
3 メリークリスマス ________
4 アイ・ラブ・ユー ________
5 ハブ・ア・ナイス・デー ________

**8** きいてみよう

Rolling And F Around

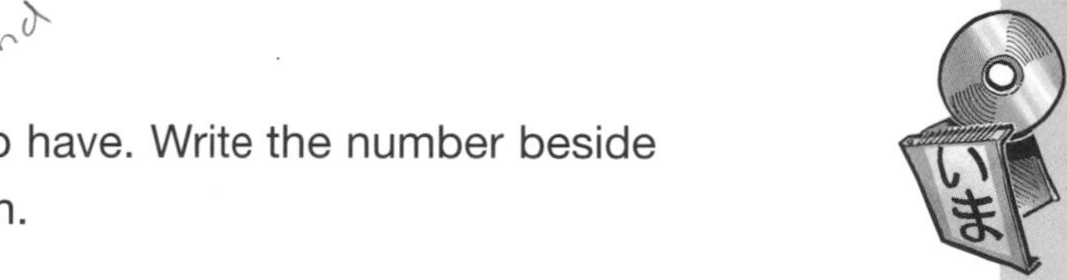


These people are thirsty and are deciding what to have. Write the number beside the picture that best represents their conversation.

**9** シン and ツソノ are possibly the trickiest カタカナ letters. Try your reading skills out on this list! Draw a line to match the カタカナ word with its English meaning.

| | |
|---|---|
| 1 シーソー | (bed) sheets |
| 2 シーツ | seat |
| 3 シャツ | see-saw |
| 4 ソーセージ | sauce |
| 5 ソース | (movie) scene |
| 6 シーン | shirt |
| 7 シート | sausages |

**10** Here is a game that Japanese children play with カタカナ letters. Add one stroke to each of the following letters to change it into another letter. The first has been done for you.

フ → ス （す）

1 フ → ______ （ら）　　2 ワ → ______ （う）

3 コ → ______ （ろ）　　4 コ → ______ （よ）

5 ノ → ______ （そ）　　6 ノ → ______ （め）

7 ソ → ______ （つ）　　8 ン → ______ （し）

9 リ → ______ （さ）　　10 ク → ______ （た）

11 ナ → ______ （ち）

**11** Fill in the last カタカナ letters on the blank tables on the inside covers of this workbook. ナイス・ワーク！

ア エ コ ゴ セ ゼ ノ ゾ ネ メ ユ リ

# カタカナ6

**1** There are lots of things in this picture that are written in カタカナ and use little ヤ, ユ and ヨ in their spelling. Write labels for these using the words below.

パジャマ　ジョギング　コンピューター　チューリップ　チョコレート
スポーツ・シューズ　ジュース　シャワー　ニュージーランド

**2** These food-related words all use little ヤ, ユ and ヨ in their spelling. Write appropriate letters in the blank spaces, using the ひらがな hints provided. Transfer the shaded letters to spell out another food.

| | | | | | | | | | |
|---|---|---|---|---|---|---|---|---|---|
| **1** marshmallow （しゅ） | マ | | | マ | ロ | | | | |
| **2** lemon squash （しゅ） | レ | モ | ン | ス | カ | ッ | | | |
| **3** mashed potatoes （しゅ） | マ | ッ | | | ポ | テ | ト | | |
| **4** casserole （きゃ） | | | セ | ロ | ー | ル | | | |
| **5** pork with ginger （じゃ） | ポ | ー | ク | ジ | ン | | | ー | |
| **6** choc mousse （ちょ） | | | コ | ム | ー | ス | | | |
| **7** tomato juice （じゅ） | ト | マ | ト | | | ー | ス | | |
| **8** menu （にゅ） | メ | | | ー | | | | | |
| **9** lamb chops （ちょ） | ラ | ム | | | ッ | プ | | | |

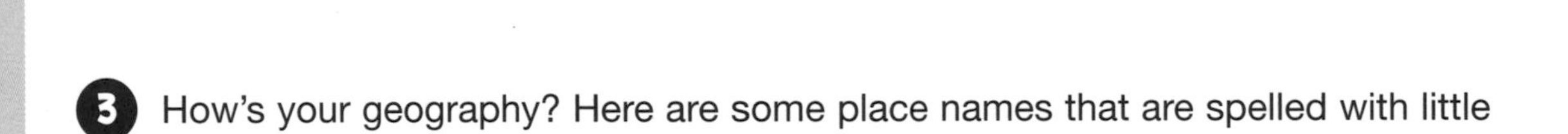

**3** How's your geography? Here are some place names that are spelled with little ヤ, ユ and ヨ. Write them in English in the spaces provided.

**1** ギリシャ ____________ **2** ホンジュラス ____________

**3** キューバ ____________ **4** ジャカルタ ____________

**5** バーミューダ ____________ **6** キャンベラ ____________

**7** ニューヨーク ____________

# カタカナ7

**1** Here is an advertisement from a supermarket encouraging people to go for a ピクニック. Complete the ad by writing labels for the items. They are listed below.

| レタス　バゲット　フィラデルフィアクリームチーズ<br>スライス10チェダー　ベーグル |
|---|

**2** カタカナ・チャレンジ!

Here are some more difficult words that have created sounds in their spelling. You can take the チャレンジ by trying to match the words with the English translations, by covering the English and trying to work out the meaning of the words, or a combination of both.
がんばって!

| | | |
|---|---|---|
| **1** | ストップウォッチ | chain store |
| **2** | ウィンドーショッピング | stop watch |
| **3** | シーディー | jelly beans |
| **4** | モッツァレラーチーズ | CD |
| **5** | ジェリービーンズ | window shopping |
| **6** | チェーンストア | mozzarella cheese |

**3** Write labels for these words. They all contain created sounds in their spelling.

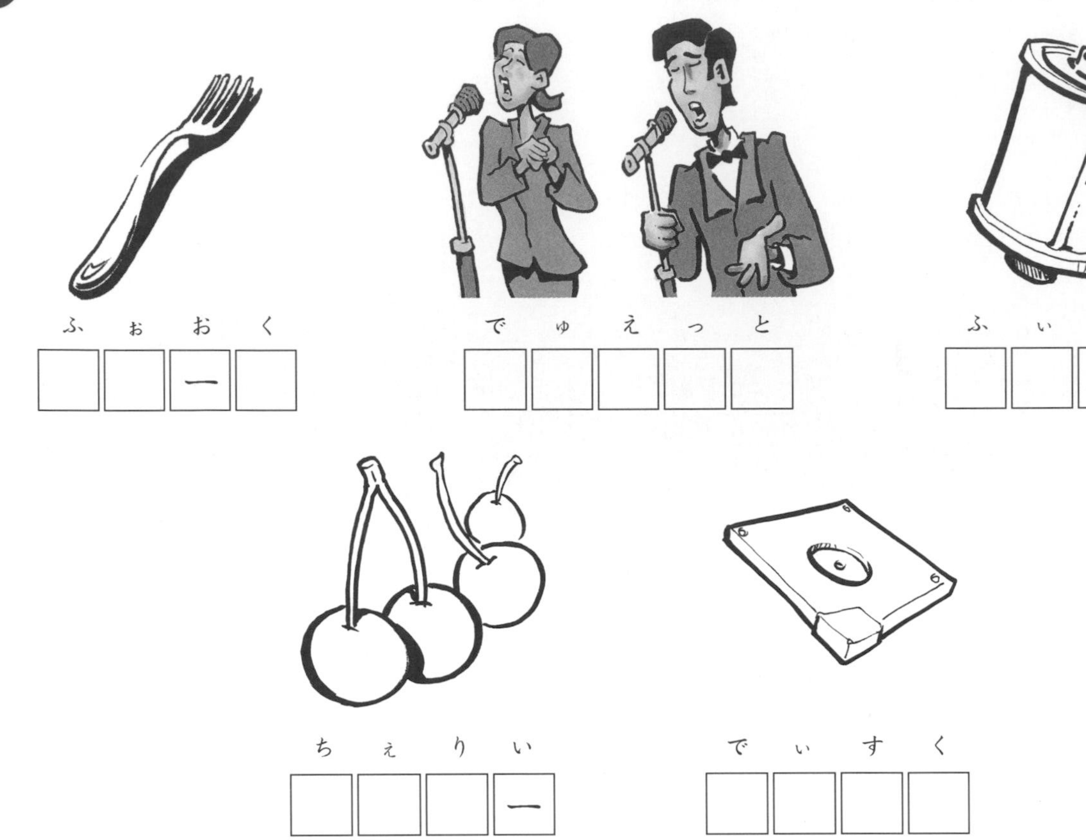


**4** These signs have been spotted around Tokyo. Read the signs and answer the following questions.

**1** A couple of old movies have been revived for a film festival of action films. What are the titles?

______________________________

______________________________

**2** What is this place called? Would you go here for シェークスピア or シェープ アップ?

______________________________

______________________________

**3** What is happening here?

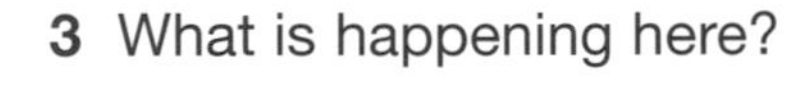

**4** Would you be more likely to buy a レモン ツリー or a レモン ティー here?

______________________________

| ツリー | tree |
|---|---|

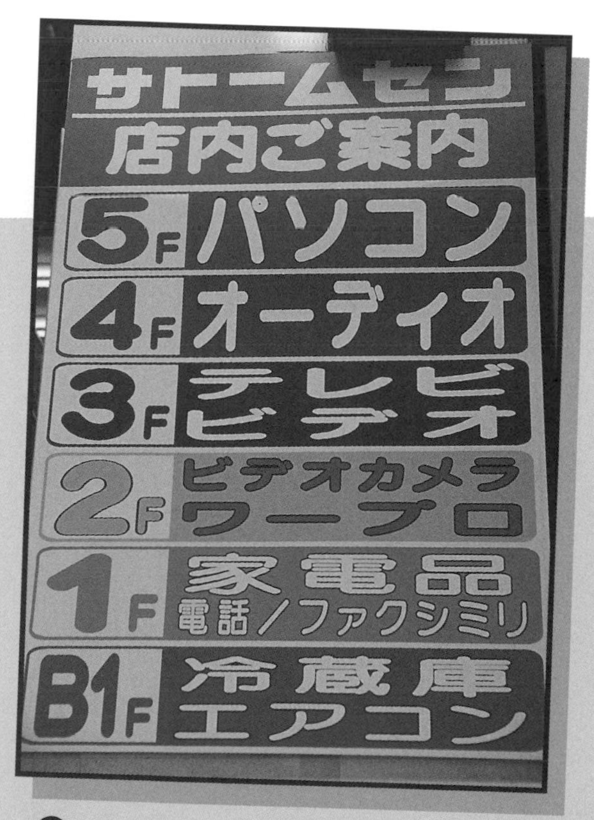


**5** This is the store guide of a large electrical store. Can you give an example, in English, of what is available on each floor?

5F (*パーソナルコンピューター)

______________________________

4F ______________________________

3F ______________________________

2F ワードプロセッサー

______________________________

1F ______________________________

B1F (*エアコンディショナー)

______________________________

# カタカナ8

**1** きいてみよう

いま

Which photo is being referred to in these conversations? Write the number of the dialogue in the appropriate box.

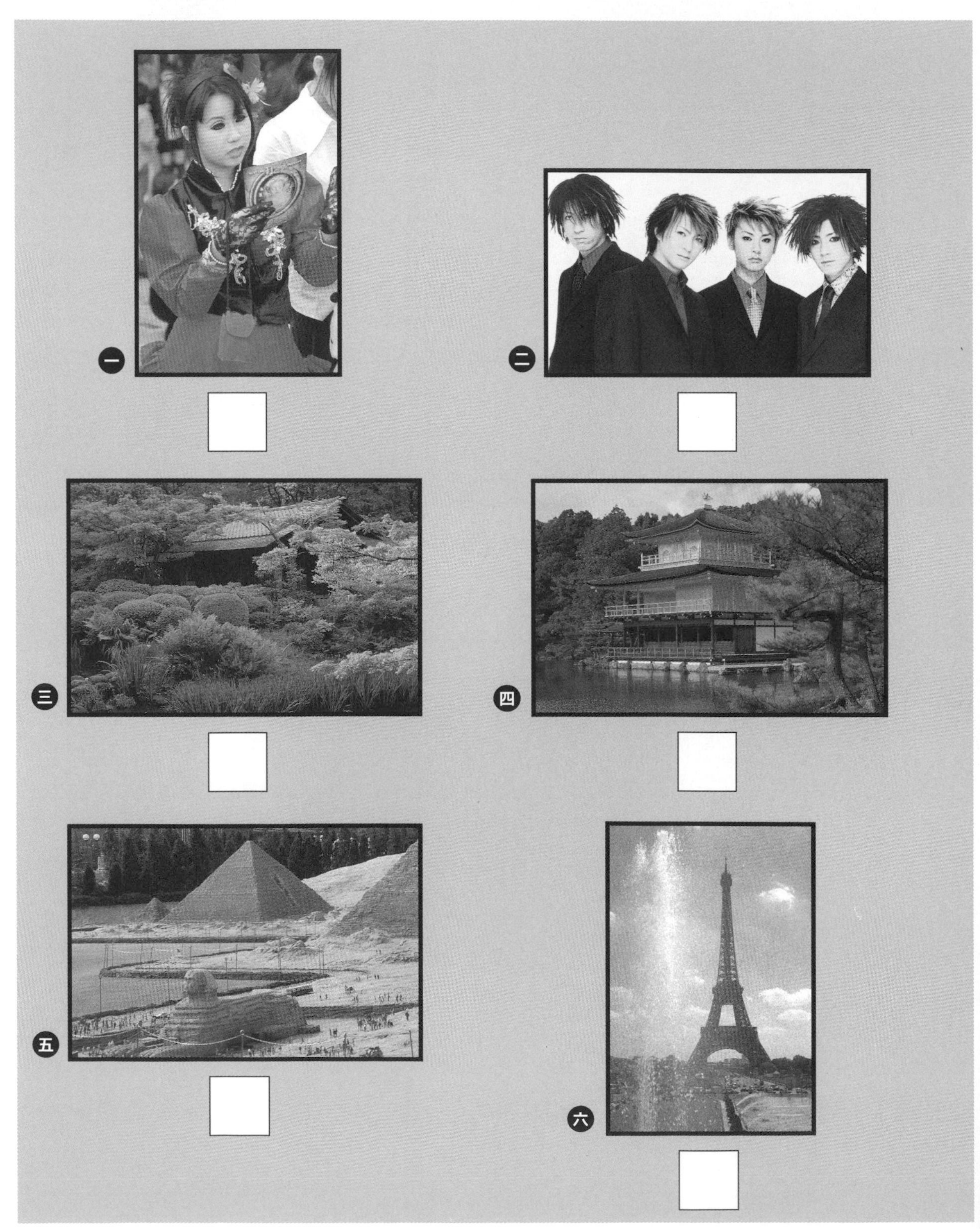

**2** Refer to the photos opposite and complete these sentences using the な adjectives that are given in the box. Remember to add な when you use a な adjective directly before a noun. Use a different adjective for each sentence.

| きれい（な） | ゆうめい（な） | しずか（な） | すてき（な） |
|---|---|---|---|
| ハンサム（な） | へん（な） | モダン（な） | ロマンチック（な） |

1 あの女の人は ______________ ですね。

2 グレイのじろさんは ______________ 男の人ですね。

3 日本のにわは ______________ です。

4 金閣寺(きんかくじ)は ______________ おてらですね。

5 エジプトで ______________ ピラミッドを見ました。

6 パリは ______________ まちですね。

**3** Complete these sentences with the names of people or places that you know.

1 ______________ はすてきです。

2 ______________ はとてもきれいです。

3 ______________ はタフな人です。(タフ (な) tough)

4 ______________ さんはゆうめいなテニスのせんしゅです。

5 ______________ さんはハンサムなスターです。

**4** If you look at the map on 35ページ of your textbook, you can see that ワールドスクウェア (World Square) is made up of various ゾーン (zones). What ゾーン would you go to to see the following things and places?

1 エンパイアステートビル ______________

2 ピラミッド ______________

3 バッキンガムきゅうでん ______________

4 ニューヨーク ______________

5 エッフェルとう ______________

**5** Where did さとしくん and めぐみさん go for their ハネムーン?
Read the story on pages 三十二〜三十五 of your 今 2 textbook and highlight the sequence of their trip.

一 さいしょに [イタリア / イギリス / エジプト] に行きました。

二 つぎ、[ギリシャ / フランス / アメリカ] に行きました。

三 [ドイツ / イタリア / エジプト] できれいなおしろを見ました。

四 [フランス / ドイツ / イギリス] に行って、ロンドンのタワーブリッジを見ました。

五 つぎ、[エジプト / ギリシャ / イタリア] に行きました。しゃしんをとりました。

六 [アメリカ / イタリア / エジプト] でピラミッドを見ました。そして、おみやげをかいました。

七 それから、[アメリカ / ドイツ / イギリス] に行きました。

Complete the sentence:

さとしくんとめぐみさんは____________________でせかいりょこうをしました。

**6** Write the phrases below in ひらがな and カタカナ on the star puzzle. The spelling for the カタカナ words is given in ひらがな, but of course you'll need to write these words in カタカナ.
One letter of each answer will fall on a shaded space. Write the shaded letters in the boxes below to complete a comment that せんせい makes.

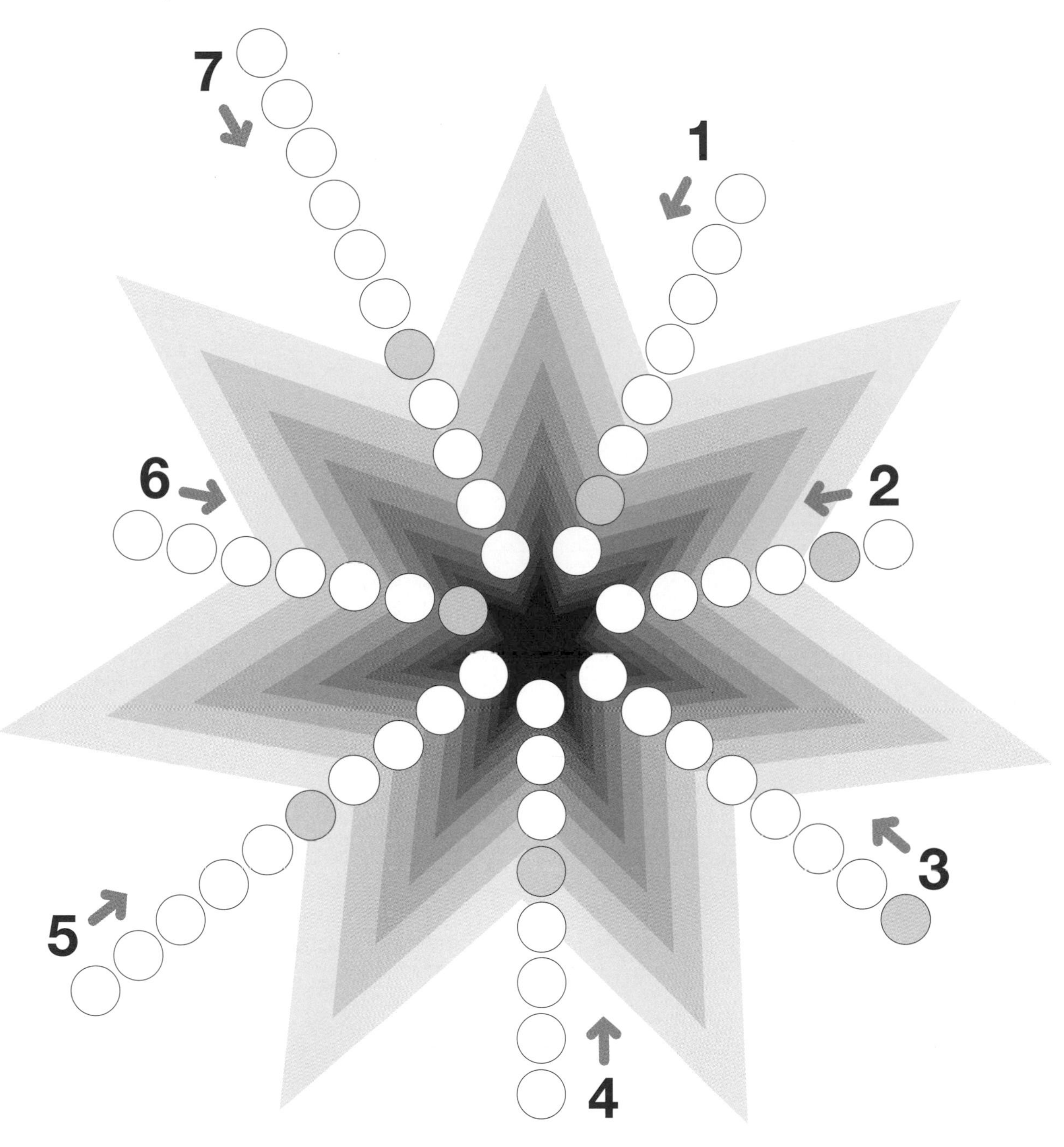


**1** pretty photo
**2** quiet garden
**3** cute souvenir
**4** famous castle
**5** romantic movie
**6** nice camera（かめら）
**7** yummy ice cream（あいすくりいむ）

|  |  |  |  |  |  |  | で | す | ね | 。 |
|---|---|---|---|---|---|---|---|---|---|---|

# 第一課

## ❶ かんじ

Practice writing these new かんじ.

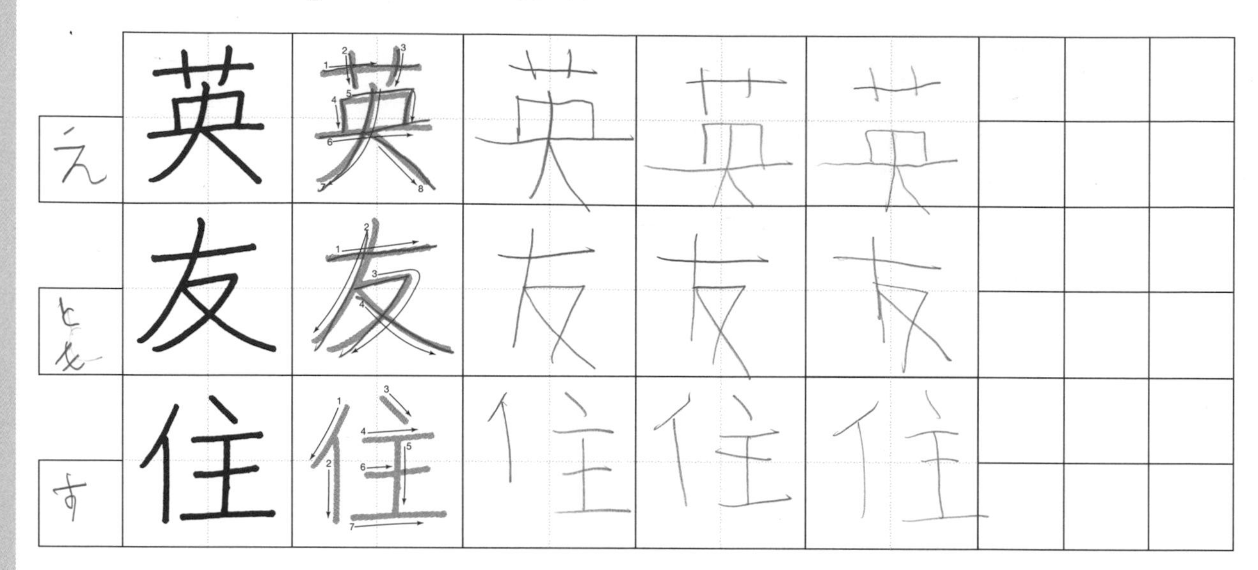


## ❷ かんじ

Draw lines to match these かんじ words to how they are read and to their meaning in English.

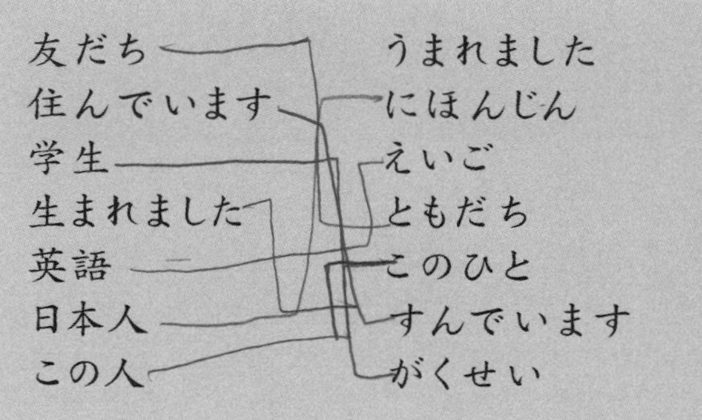


## ❸ かんじ

This is Ben and his friend 友子. Complete the information about them by writing the words given in the underlined sections in かんじ. You may have to write a bit of ひらがな to complete some words.

この＿＿(ひと)はベンです。ブルームで＿＿＿＿(うまれ)ました。

＿＿(いま)、スカイに＿＿＿＿(すんで)います。

ベンくんはオーストラリア＿＿(じん)です。もちろん、

＿＿＿＿(えいご)をはなします。＿＿＿＿＿＿(にほんご)もすこしはなします。

＿＿＿＿＿＿(ともだち)の＿＿＿＿(ともこ)さんは＿＿＿＿＿＿(にほんじん)です。

＿＿＿＿(ふたり)はテニスがすきです。

## ❹ かんじ

Write the number of strokes (from 1–8) in the box beside each of these かんじ and then show that you know it by writing a word that contains that かんじ.

一 生 ☐ ______________ 二 住 ☐ ______________

三 英 ☐ ______________ 四 友 ☐ ______________

五 一 ☐ ______________ 六 人 ☐ ______________

七 行 ☐ ______________ 八 大 ☐ ______________

# パートA

**Birthplaces, residences, nationalities and languages**

## ❺ かいてみよう

Complete the following table to show the nationality and languages spoken in the country given.

| くに | ～人 | ～語 |
|---|---|---|
| アメリカ | アメリカ人 | 英語 |
| イギリス | イギリス人 | 英語 |
| イタリア | イタリア人 | イタリア語 |
| オーストラリア | オーストラリア人 | 英語 |
| ギリシャ | | |
| シンガポール | | |
| ちゅうごく | | |
| 日本 | | |
| ニュージーランド | | |

第一課

## 6 きいてみようA

These students are part of an international exchange group. They are being asked where they were born. Circle the country of their birth as they give the information.

一 あきな

Japan USA England

______________________

二 アン・ソフィ

England Italy France

______________________

三 パスカル

USA Canada France

______________________

四 レオナード

Italy Germany Australia

______________________

五 アリ

England Indonesia China

______________________

六 レーリー

Japan Australia China

______________________

七 ダンヤル

Germany France Italy

______________________

八 ローラ

Canada Indonesia Australia

______________________

## 7 きいてみようB

This time the students are being asked where they live now. Write the name of the place on the line beneath each student's name.

## 8 かいてみよう

Look at the information given about these people and use it to answer the questions below. The first has been done for you.

1 さゆりさんはどこで生まれましたか。
日本で生まれました。

2 今、どこに住んでいますか。
日本のよこはまに住んでいます。

3 さゆりさんは日本人ですか。
はい、日本人です。

なまえ　：さゆり
生まれ　：日本
住まい　：日本、横浜（よこはま）
こくせき：日本

なまえ　：ジョン
生まれ　：アメリカ
住まい　：アメリカ、シカゴ
こくせき：アメリカ

4 ジョンさんはどこで生まれましたか。
アメリカで生まれました

5 今、どこに住んでいますか。
アメリカに住んでいます

6 ジョンさんはアメリカ人ですか。
はい、アメリカ人です。

7 イザベラさんはどこで生まれましたか。
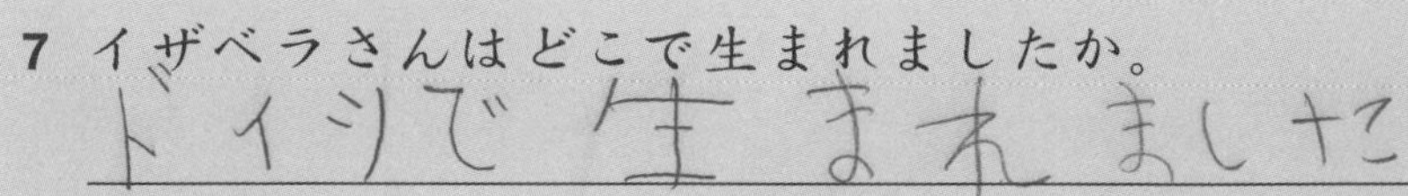
ドイツで生まれました

8 今、どこに住んでいますか。
イタリアに住んでいます。

9 イザベラさんはイタリア人ですか。
いいえ　ドイツ人です。

なまえ　：イザベラ
生まれ　：ドイツ
住まい　：イタリア、ペルジア
こくせき：ドイツ

なまえ　：ジェーソン
生まれ　：オーストラリア
住まい　：ニュージーランド、オークランド
こくせき：オーストラリア

10 ジェーソンくんはどこで生まれましたか。

11 今もオーストラリアに住んでいますか。

12 ジェーソンくんはニュージーランド人ですか。

## 9 かいてみよう

Here is some more information about the people pictured on the previous page – this time it is about what languages they speak. Answer the question below using the information. Write complete sentences.

（さゆりさん）は何語をはなしますか。

さゆり

日本語、英語、
フランス語（すこし）

一 さゆりさんは日本語と英語とFrenchははなします。

ジョン

英語、ちゅうごく語

二 ジヨンさんは英語とちゆうごく語ははなします。

イザベラ

ドイツ語、イタリア語、
スペイン語（すこし）

三 

ジェーソンくん

英語、日本語（すこし）

四 

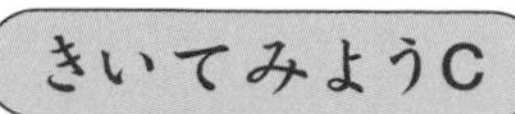

## 10 きいてみようC

友田(だ)せん生 is looking at the list of new overseas students who have enrolled in her Japanese conversation class. Listen as she discusses the students with the enrollment officer and jot down the nationality of each student in English, as well as what language or languages they speak.

| クラス リスト | | |
|---|---|---|
| なまえ | 〜人<br>nationality | 〜語<br>language |
| 1 ジェームズ・ソープ (James Thorp) | | |
| 2 フィービ・ウェッブ (Phoebe Webb) | | |
| 3 チェン・コ (Chen Ko) | | |
| 4 ピータ・コリンズ (Peta Collins) | | |
| 5 クリス・フレミング (Chris Fleming) | | |
| 6 キム・ジュン (Kim Ji-eun ) | | |
| 7 カール・スズキ (Carl Suzuki) | | |
| 8 ソンヤ・シュルツ (Sonja Schulz) | | |
| 9 イマム・スサント (Imam Susanto) | | |
| 10 モリー・ドイル (Molly Doyle) | | |

## 11 かいてみよう

Fill in the following profile about yourself.

なまえ：____________________

生まれ：____________________

住まい：____________________

こくせき：____________________

ことば：____________________

| | |
|---|---|
| 生まれ | birthplace |
| 住まい | residence |
| こくせき | nationality, country |
| ことば | language/s |

## 12 かいてみよう

Now answer the following questions about yourself.

1 どこで生まれましたか。 ____________________

2 今、どこに住んでいますか。 ____________________

3 オーストラリア人ですか。 ____________________

4 何語をはなしますか。 ____________________

# パートB

**Describing yourself and your friends**

**13** かいてみよう

ジョセフくん is going to the airport to pick up さえ子さん, a Japanese exchange student who will be staying with his family. She's written and told him what she looks like. He's also written and given her a description of himself. Read their descriptions and sketch ジョセフくん and さえ子さん meeting at the airport. Also, draw some speech bubbles and write what ジョセフくん and さえ子さん might say when they meet for the first time and introduce themselves.

**さえ子さんから**

... わたしはせがひくいです。
かみがながいです。
そして、かみがくろいです。
めがねをかけています。
ジョセフくんはどうですか。
...

**ジョセフくんから**

... ぼくはせがたかいです。
ぼくもかみがながいです。
かみがきんぱつです。ぼくは
めがねをかけていません。
でも、よくサングラスを
かけています。
...

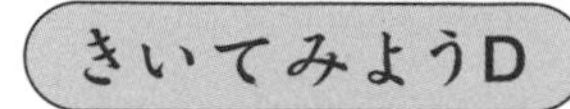


People are having trouble telling these twins apart. The name of one twin is given below each picture. Listen as someone describes that twin and draw a line to show which person is being referred to.

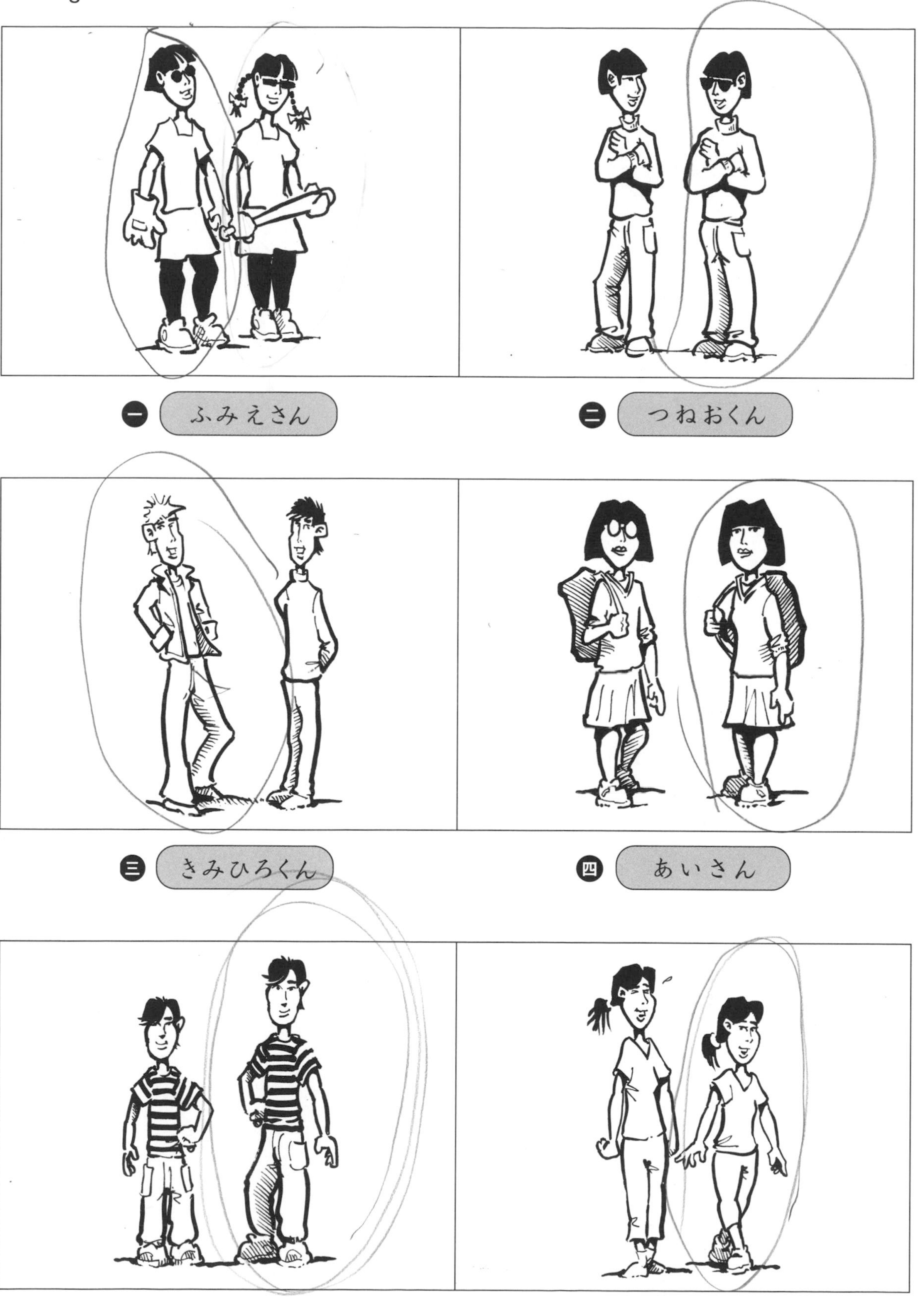

## 15 かいてみよう

Write a description of the people pictured here. Comment on their height, hair color and length, and whether or not they wear glasses.

ソフィアさん

まなさん

うえださん

つねおくん

16 かいてみよう

What do you look like? Are you tall? What color is your hair? Is it long or short? Do you wear glasses? Write a short description of yourself in the space below.

# パートC

Putting it together

17 かいてみよう

Read the first page of the story 「トーナメントのチーム」on 40ページ of your textbook and complete the profiles of Akina and Sayuri.

| | |
|---|---|
| **Name:** *Akina Murai* | **Name:** *Sayuri Tago* |
| **Grade level:** | **Grade level:** |
| **Place of birth:** | **Place of birth:** |
| **Current residence:** | **Club:** |
| **Club:** | **Language/s spoken:** |

Now write a description in 日本語 of either あきなさん or さゆりさん.

## 18 よんでみよう

Read the story about the トーナメントのチーム which begins on 40 ページ of your textbook and choose the alternative which best describes the person mentioned.

| | | | |
|---|---|---|---|
| 1 | あきなさんは、 | 東京（とうきょう）<br>ロンドン<br>ハワイ | に住んでいました。 |
| 2 | さゆりさんは、 | イギリス<br>日本<br>アメリカ | で生まれました。 |
| 3 | あきなさんもさゆりさんも | テニスぶのメンバー<br>中（ちゅう）学二年生<br>10さい | です。 |
| 4 | えみ子さんは | かみがながいです。<br>せがたかいです。<br>めがねをかけています。 | |
| 5 | ゆかりさんは | せがひくい<br>テニスがへた<br>かみがみじかい | です。 |
| 6 | さゆりさんは | のどがかわきました。<br>ボレーがだめです。<br>テニスがじょうずです。 | |

## 19 よんでみよう

Read the following statements about えみ子さん, one of the tennis team members from Keio Shonan Fujisawa Junior High, and decide whether they are true or false. Highlight ○（まる）for true or ✕（ばつ）for false.

**えみ子さんは:**

| | | | |
|---|---|---|---|
| 1 | 二年生です。 | ○ | ✕ |
| 2 | めがねをかけています。 | ○ | ✕ |
| 3 | せがひくいです。 | ○ | ✕ |
| 4 | かみがあかいです。 | ○ | ✕ |
| 5 | かみがみじかいです。 | ○ | ✕ |
| 6 | テニスぶのキャプテンです。 | ○ | ✕ |
| 7 | テニスがじょうずです。 | ○ | ✕ |
| 8 | トーナメントのチームのメンバーです。 | ○ | ✕ |

## 20 きいてみようE

Use a highlighter to track the sequence of this conversation.

| ひろみさん、<br>ひろしくん、 | しゃしんを見せて。 |
|---|---|

| どうぞ。 | バスケットボールぶ<br>すいえいぶ<br>テニスぶ | のメンバーのしゃしんです。 |
|---|---|---|

| おもしろい<br>すてきな | しゃしんですね。この | きれいな<br>ハンサムな | 人はだれですか。 |
|---|---|---|---|

| 友だちの | まりさん<br>ひろくん | です。とてもいい人ですよ！ |
|---|---|---|

| そうですか。 | まりさん<br>ひろくん | は | かみが | ちゃいろ<br>あかい<br>みじかい<br>ながい | ですね。 |
|---|---|---|---|---|---|

| そうですね。そして、 | まりさん<br>ひろくん | は | せがたかい<br>せがひくい | です。 |
|---|---|---|---|---|

| かっこいいサングラスをかけていますね。 |
|---|

| そうですね。 | まりさん<br>ひろくん | はかっこいいですよ。そして、 | 英語<br>イタリア語<br>ちゅうごく語 | がじょうずです。 |
|---|---|---|---|---|

| そうですか。 | わたし<br>ぼく | は | 英語<br>イタリア語<br>ちゅうごく語 | がすきです。すこしはなします。 |
|---|---|---|---|---|

| しょうかいしてください！どこに住んでいますか。 |
|---|

| しょうかいしてください！ | Please introduce me! |
|---|---|

| あのね、 | まりさん<br>ひろくん | は日本で生まれました。 |
|---|---|---|

| せんしゅうまで、 | 東京（とうきょう）<br>大阪（おおさか）<br>横浜（よこはま） | に住んでいました。でも、今、 | ロンドン<br>ローマ<br>ホンコン | に住んでいます。 |
|---|---|---|---|---|

| ロンドン<br>ローマ<br>ホンコン | に住んでいますか!? そうですか。ざんねんですね。 |
|---|---|

## 21 かいてみよう

Here are some pictures taken during the selection of the tennis team. What are these people saying or thinking? Choose appropriate expressions from the list below and write them in the blank bubbles.

水、どうぞ！　じゃんけんポン！
サンキュー　チェッ！
のどがかわきました

## 22 パズルあそび

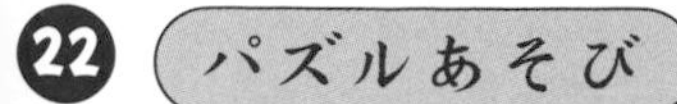

この女の子のなまえは何ですか。

Write the information about this girl on the puzzle in ひらがな, カタカナ and かんじ and the answer to the question will appear in the shaded letters.

1 She speaks Japanese.

2 She was born in Japan.

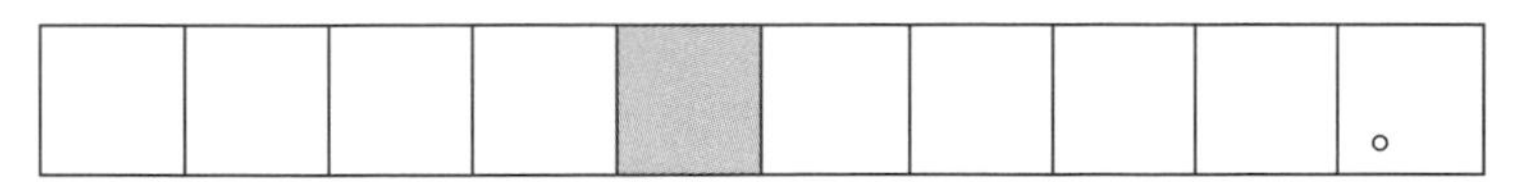

3 She loves the movies.

4 Her father is Japanese.

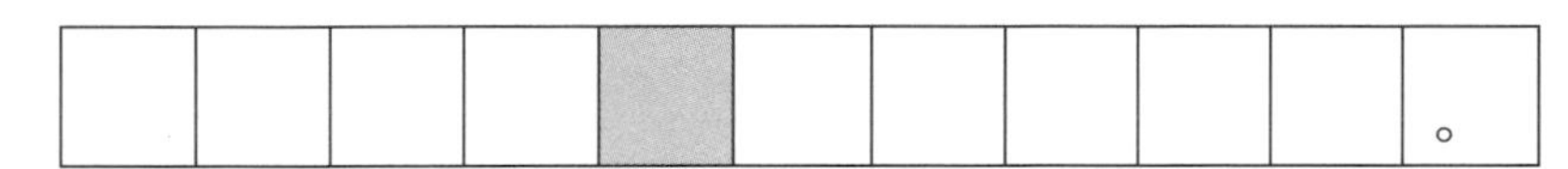

5 Her mother is French.

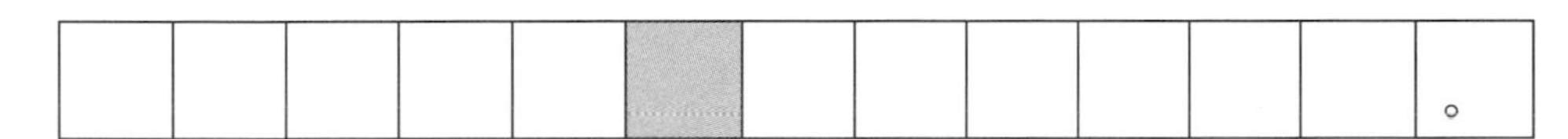

6 They live in France now.

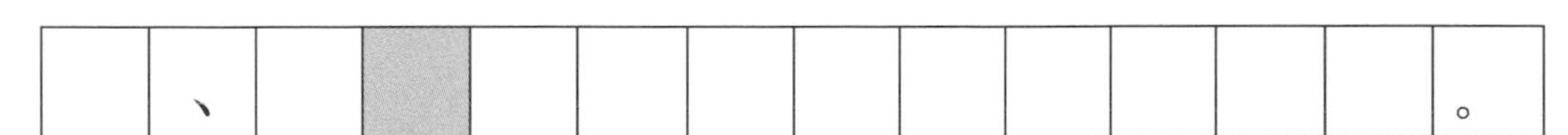

7 She speaks a little French.

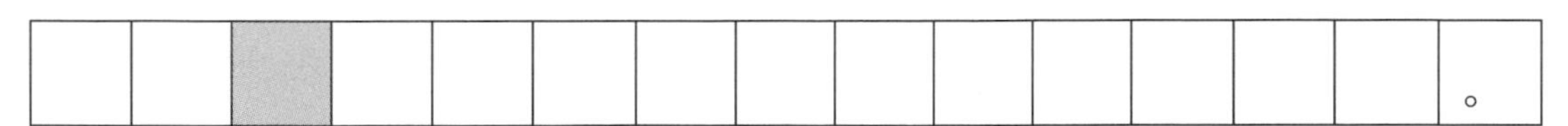

8 She's got brown hair.

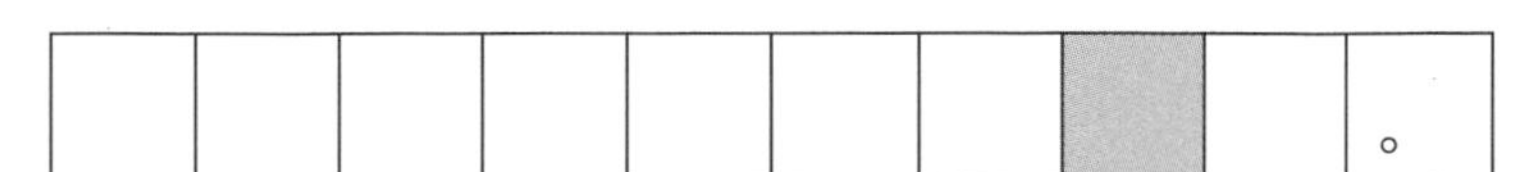

9 She's tall.

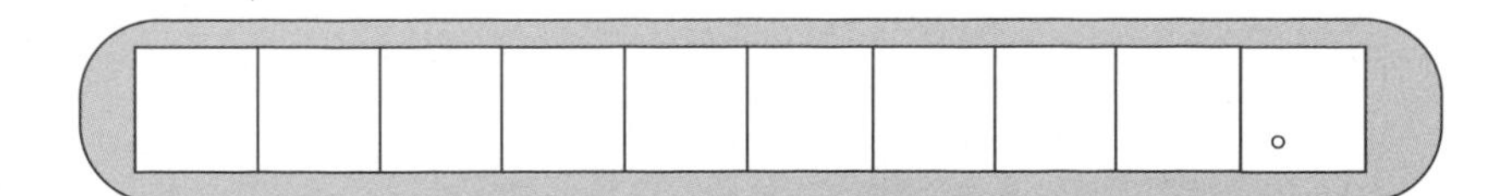

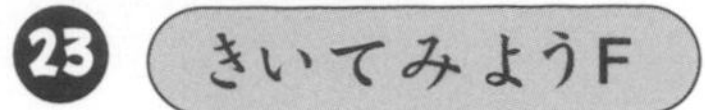


These students are telling you a bit about themselves. Practice your note-taking skills and jot down as much information as you can about each one.

**24** You have been asked to design a web page for someone you like – a TV star, movie star or pop star, or perhaps your sporting hero. They might even be your best friend... Do some research and prepare a sample page (with a picture of the person) which gives information such as name, age, where they were born, what nationality they are, where they currently live, what languages they speak, what they look like, their interests, and what makes them special for you.

**25** かいてみよう

Here are some じゃんけん results. Complete the statements about whether the picture shows a かち (win) or まけ (loss) for グー, チョキ or パー.

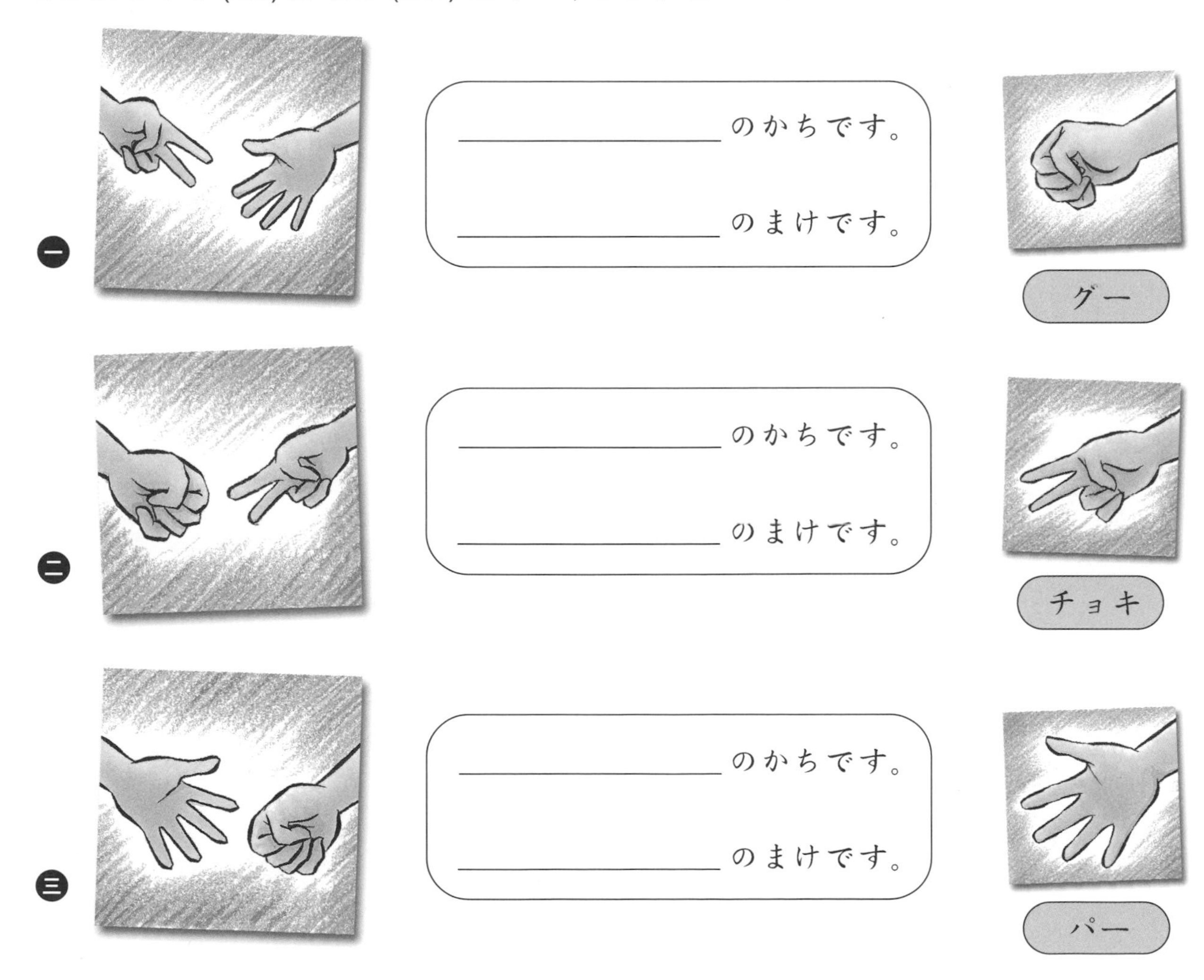


Now try a 'best of five' game. Chant じゃん－けん－ポン as you move your hand up and down. Make your グー, チョキ or パー shape as you say ポン.
When you both put out the same shape, say あいこでしょう and make your shape after あいこでしょう. You can keep saying あいこでしょう if you keep putting out matching shapes until you get a winner.

## 26 きいてみようG

Play the「だれですか」ゲーム with ひろゆき. He will tell you a friend's name and then some information about them. After listening to the information, decide which person in each group is ひろゆき's friend and circle the appropriate person.
Hint: you can eliminate people from the group as you hear the descriptions.

一

二

三

四

五

六

# 第二課



## 1 かんじ

Practice writing these new かんじ.

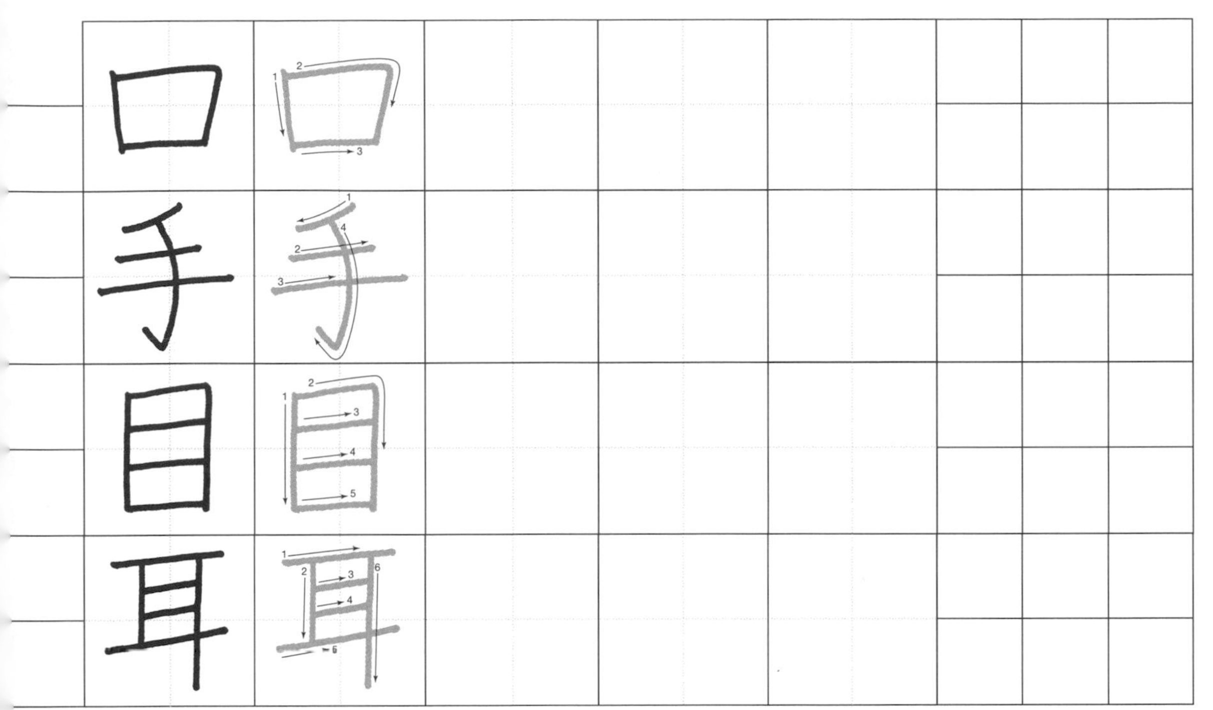


## 2 かんじ

Use the new かんじ to complete this picture. →

## 3 かんじ

Here are some Japanese expressions that use the words for hand, eye, ear and mouth. Read the meanings of the expressions and fill in each blank with an appropriate かんじ.

1 ________ がわるいです。

I have poor eyesight.

2 ________ をかして。

Lend me an ear!

3 ________ がうるさい…。

People will gossip…

4 ________ をかして。

Lend me a hand.

# パートA

Health and sickness

## ④ かいてみよう

Label the body parts on this statue. Since he's a bit 'thin', you might have to 'flesh him out' so that your labels are clear.

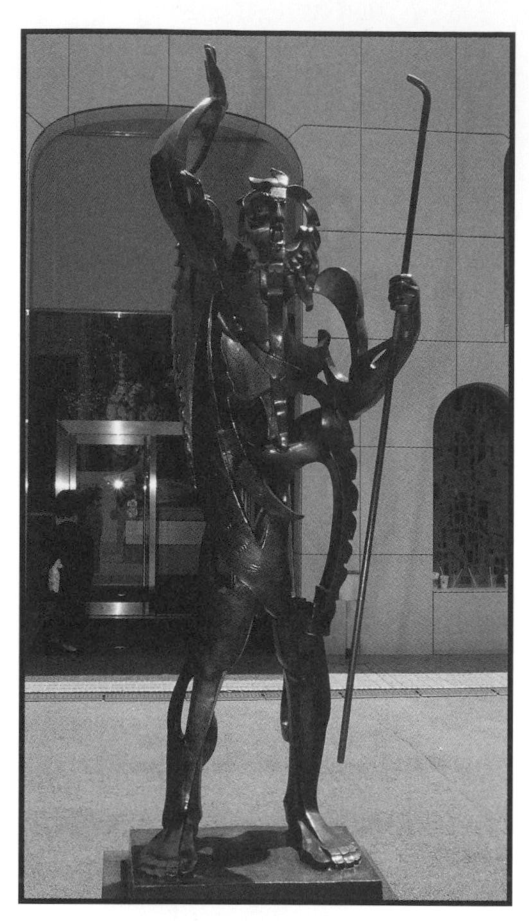

## ⑤ きいてみようA

いま

Ouch! Where have these people hurt themselves?
Listen as they explain and circle the appropriate word.

| | | | | |
|---|---|---|---|---|
| 1 | eye | ear | nose | mouth |
| 2 | ankle | finger | toe | hand |
| 3 | nose | neck | mouth | tooth |
| 4 | ankle | leg | wrist | finger |
| 5 | tummy | back | head | face |
| 6 | eye | hand | wrist | ear |

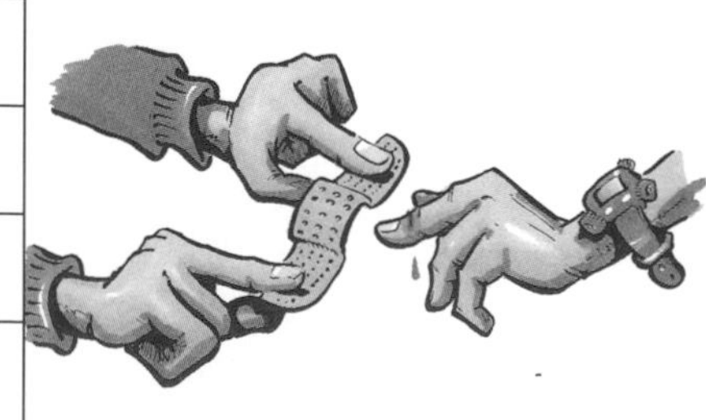

## 6 かいてみよう

The Keio tennis team had a lot of sick and injured players on the トーナメントの日. Of course, everyone asked them どうしたんですか. Look at these pictures and write in the speech bubble what each player said.

## 7 きいてみようB

What a sick-looking lot! Listen as these people are asked what is wrong with them and write the number of the conversation next to the appropriate picture.

## 8 きいてみようC

Listen as the sick and injured people from the previous page are given advice about what to do. Put a check in the appropriate column. Sometimes they are given more than one piece of advice so check all relevant columns.

| | Put on a Band-Aid | Go to bed early | Take some medicine |
|---|---|---|---|
| 一 じゅん子さん | | | |
| 二 まほさん | | | |
| 三 まさとくん | | | |
| 四 ようすけくん | | | |
| 五 さわ子さん | | | |
| 六 けんとうくん | | | |

## 9 かいてみよう

You have run into your friends みどりさん and だいいちくん and notice that they are in pain. Write a dialogue of the conversation that could take place – find out what the matter is, be sympathetic, offer some 'medical' advice...

みどりさん

___

___

___

___

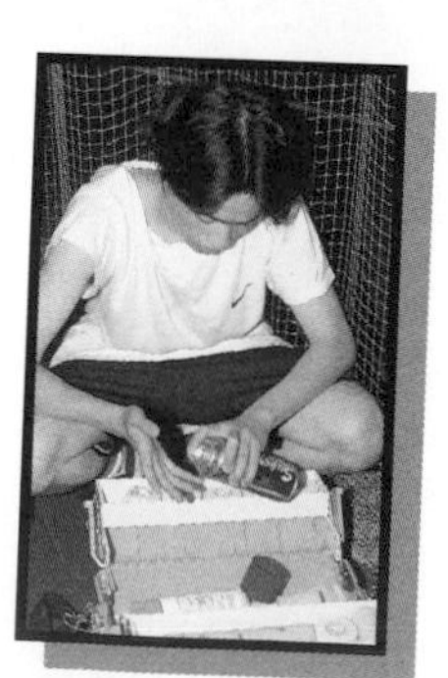

だいいちくん

___

___

___

___

**10** かいてみよう

Your friend, Chris, is always looking for ways to get out of doing physical activities. He wants you to write an excuse for him in 日本語, so that he can just relax at the 日本語のキャンプ. Here is his note. Write an excuse in the space provided.

せん生へ、
すみません。今日、クリスは
すいえいができません。

______________________________

______________________________

クリスの母より

**11** かいてみよう

The teachers at the camp are most sympathetic towards Chris and they insist on him taking medicine, putting on a Band-Aid, going to bed early... (They probably don't believe お母さん wrote the note!) Write what せん生 said and then recommended for Chris.

______________________________

______________________________

______________________________

______________________________

______________________________

**12** かいてみよう

あ、ひろくん、かわいそうに... What has put ひろくん in bed?
Write the following 'medical' sentences on the puzzle in ひらがな and カタカナ. Then unscramble the 'star' letters to work out what is wrong with ひろくん.

| | |
|---|---|
| 1 What's the matter? | 4 Take some medicine. |
| 2 I've got a headache. | 5 Go to bed early. |
| 3 I feel sick. | 6 Put a Band-Aid on it. |

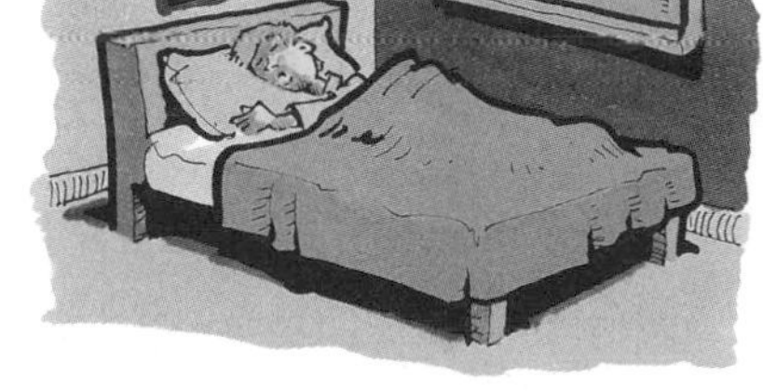

1 □□□✱□□□□。

2 □□□✱□□□□□□。

3 □□✱□□□□□□□。

4 □□□□□□□□□□✱。

5 ✱□□□□□□□□。

6 □□□□□□□□□□□□□✱。

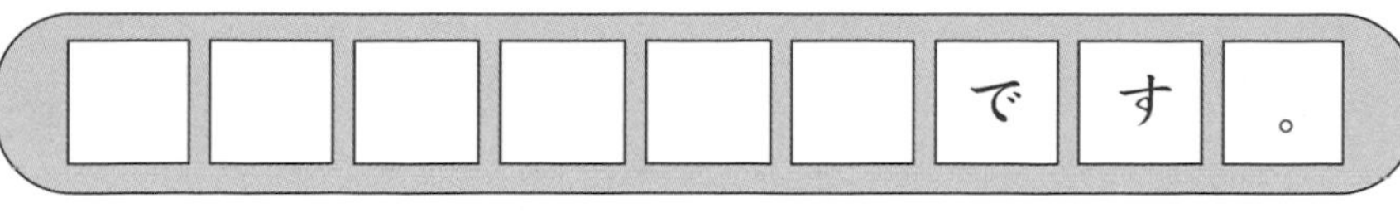
□□□□□□です。

# パートB

Where is she?
Where is it?

## 13 かいてみよう

Complete these sentences with either います or あります.

1 せん生はきょうしつに ________________ 。

2 わたしの日本語のワークブックはうちに ________________ 。

3 お母さんはにわに ________________ 。

4 ねこもにわに ________________ 。

5 友だちはこうえんに ________________ 。

6 としょかんはまちに ________________ 。

7 けしゴムはどこに ________________ か。

8 ぼくのじてんしゃはこうえんに ________________ 。

## 14 かいてみよう

You have a bad case of domestic blindness. You drive your mom mad with questions when you can't see things that are right under your nose – or is it just that you find it easier to ask than to look...? She might be less irritated with you if you put your questions in 日本語. You're doing homework, right?
Here are some questions for you to start with.

1 Mom, where are my sport shoes?

______________________________________________

2 Mom, where are my socks?（ソックス）

______________________________________________

3 Mom, where is the remote control?（リモコン）

______________________________________________

4 Mom, where are the chocolate cookies?（チョコレートビスケット）

______________________________________________

## 15 きいてみようD

おさむ is always losing things. Listen as he asks different people where his things are and circle the picture that shows their response.

一

二

三

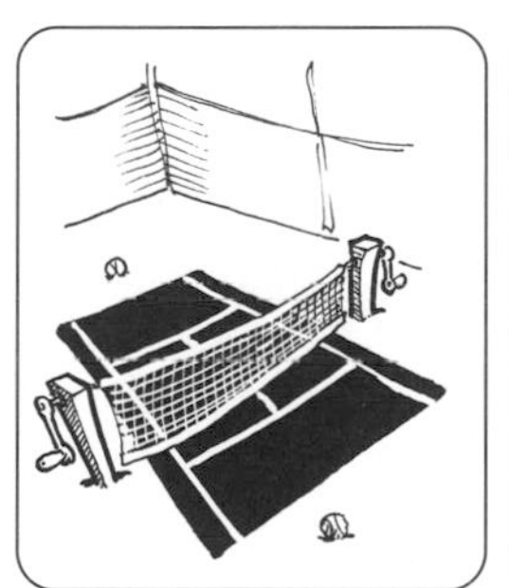

四

**16** かいてみよう

Joe gets around! Where is he in these pictures? Write a sentence explaining where he is.
ジョーくんはどこにいますか。

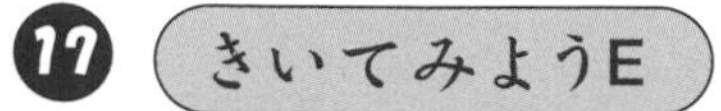


Where are they? Sometimes you just can't find your friend or pet.
Listen as these people search for friends and pets and circle where they are.

一

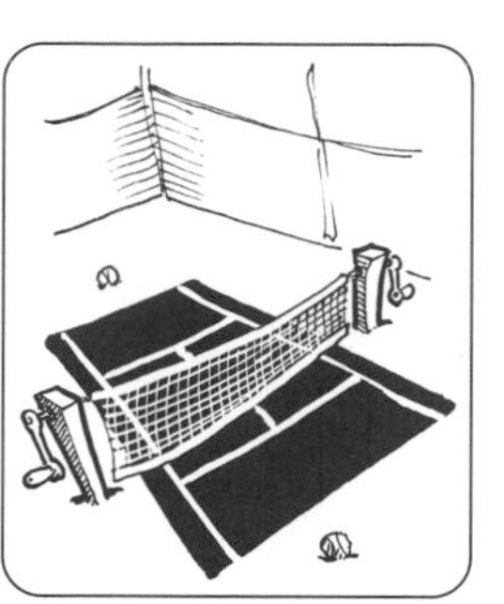

二

三

四

**18** Choose a time when people in your family are at different places and write a 'snapshot' of this time. Begin with the date, day and time. You can use English (or a dictionary or せん生) for any words that you don't know.

# パートC

**Putting it together**

**19** かいてみよう

Read the まんが, テニスのトーナメント which begins on 58 ページ of your 今2 textbook and answer the following questions. Answer in complete sentences.

1 今日はいいてんきですか。

______________________________

2 おうえんだんはどこにいますか。

______________________________

3 テニスのチームのキャプテンのなまえは何ですか。

______________________________

4 さゆりさんはどうしたんですか。

______________________________

5 まほさんは、今日、テニスをしますか。

______________________________

6 えみ子さんは何年生ですか。

7 えみ子さんはどこにいますか。

8 えみ子さんのテニスシューズはどこにありますか。

9 さいしょのシングルスははる子さんのかちですか。まけですか。

10 さいごのシングルスはえみ子さんのかちですか。まけですか。

## 20 かいてみよう

Read the まんが, テニスのトーナメント, which begins on 58 ページ of your textbook, and find words and expressions which you can use in the following situations.

1 You want to cheer on your team and tell them to hang in there!

2 You miss a really easy shot when playing basketball.

3 You want to praise someone on their great shot.

4 You comment that her serve is strong.

5 You comment that the team is no good today.

6 You comment that your team tried hard today, but...

7 You tell someone that it was your team's win today. Fantastic!

## 21 かいてみよう

トムくん is telling you a bit about himself and what he did yesterday. He wasn't sure what particles to use (unlike you, he mixes them up) so he just smudged over them. Show him what particles are used in the smudgy sections. Choose from に, で and を.

ぼくはトムです。日本 ____ 生まれました。
今、オーストラリア ____ 住んでいます。
きのう友だちの友子さんのうち ____ 行きました。
友子さんのうち ____ ビデオゲーム ____ しました。たのしかったです。

4時 ____ バス ____ うち ____ かえりました。
ぼくはかぞくとうち ____ ばんごはん ____ たべました。

ばんごはんのあと、いもうととテレビ ____ 見ました。それから、へや ____ しゅくだい ____ しました。しゅくだいはちょっとむずかしかったです。でも、がんばりました。

今、ぼくはへや ____ います。ぼくはこのへやがすきです。

## 22 かいてみよう

しょう子さん's dog, ケーちゃん, has gone missing and she has written a notice to put in the window of a nearby shop. The man in the shop says that her notice is too long – what information do you think she should delete?

### いぬがいなくなりました！

- いぬのなまえはケーちゃんです。
- 友だちのうちで生まれました。
- ケーちゃんはちいさいいぬです。
- ケーちゃんは目が大きいです。
- ケーちゃんは耳がながいです。
- しっぽもながいです。(しっぽ tail)
- ケーちゃんはさんぽがすきです。
- はる子さんのいぬとよくあそびます。
- ケーちゃんはパルのドッグフードが大すきです。
- ケーちゃんはとてもすてきないぬです。
- わたしはケーちゃんが大すきです。

## 23 きいてみようF

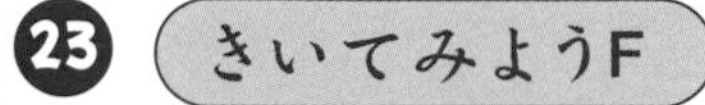

Listen to these short conversations and write the number which best represents each conversation in the box under the appropriate picture.

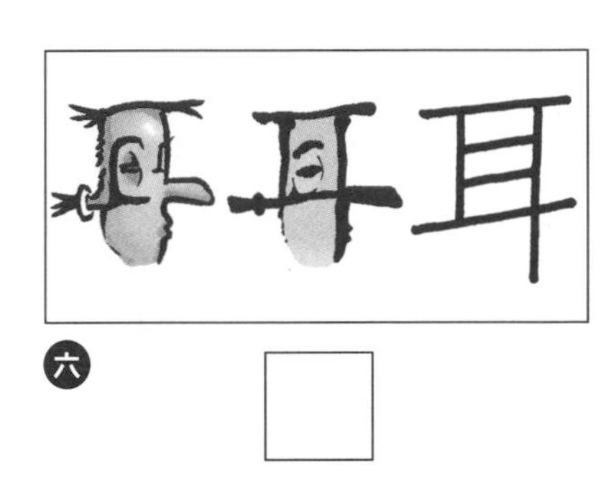


六

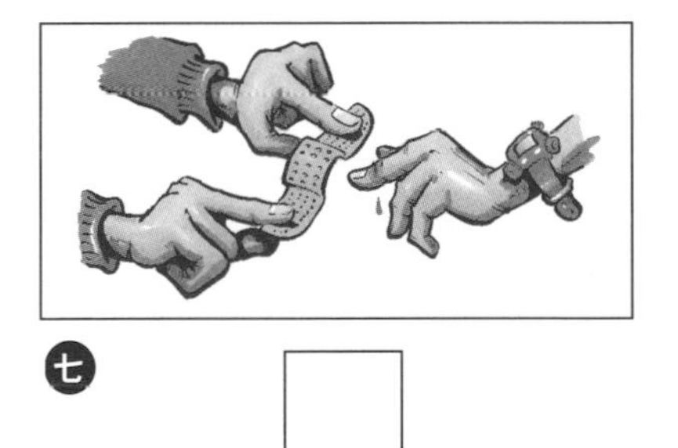

七

## 24 パズルあそび

Think about the meanings of these words and then highlight the one that does not belong in each group.

1 手　耳　目　口　はな

2 くび　あしくび　手くび　ゆび　あしのゆび

3 学校　うち　きょうしつ　としょかん

4 スポーツバッグ　テニスボール　シングルス　ラケット　テニスシューズ

5 チーム　バックハンド　ボレー　ロブ　サーブ

## 25 パズルあそび

All of these words are hidden in the puzzle below. Find them either horizontally or vertically and mark them on the puzzle. Ten letters will remain to spell out what is wrong with せん生.

| | | |
|---|---|---|
| first, last, yesterday | throat, wrist, tooth, ear | poor you!, disappointing! |
| there isn't (thing) | library, classroom, room, park | no good |
| cheering squad | win, loss | medicine, sore |

| | | | | | | | | | | |
|---|---|---|---|---|---|---|---|---|---|---|
| さ | さ | い | し | ょ | と | し | ょ | か | ん | き |
| い | か | わ | い | そ | う | に | く | の | ど | ょ |
| ご | き | だ | め | い | み | か | す | は | ぶ | う |
| て | く | び | ん | た | み | ち | り | が | わ | し |
| ざ | ん | ね | ん | い | る | こ | う | え | ん | つ |
| へ | い | あ | り | ま | せ | ん | き | の | う | ん |
| や | で | ま | け | す | お | う | え | ん | だ | ん |

## 1 かんじ

Practice writing these new かんじ.

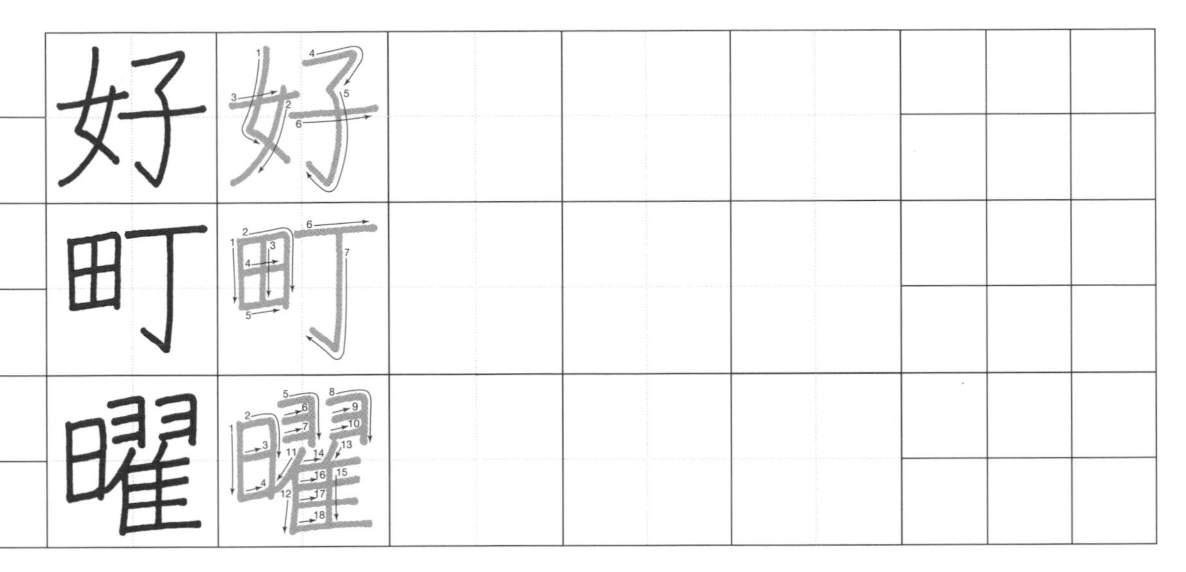


### しってる？

You have probably noticed that in the かんじ, 好き and 曜, the part on the left is a familiar かんじ. This part of the character gives us some idea of its meaning. What can you say about the meaning of 曜 and 時, which both have 日 on the left side? Can you make any connection with 女 and 好? How about the connection with 女 in these words: 妹(いもうと), 姉(あね)?

Note that when a かんじ is used as part of another かんじ, its shape changes a bit to fit the shape of the new かんじ.

## 2 かんじ

こうじくん has been on the phone again to his girlfriend. How do we know? Because he has doodled on the phone message pad. Look at what he has written, then try a doodle of your own, in 日本語, with the name of someone you like.

友子

好き好き好き

かわいい

大好き

**3** かんじ

Can you really write 曜 and use the correct stroke order? Test yourself by writing on the stroke numbers.

**4** かんじ

Fill in the calendar for this month by writing in the month and the days of the week. You could also review the days of the month. Remember them? 一日（ついたち）, 二日（ふつか）...

| | | | | | | |
|---|---|---|---|---|---|---|
| | | | | | | |
| | | | | | | |
| | 1 | 2 | 3 | 4 | 5 | 6 |
| 7 | 8 | 9 | 10 | 11 | 12 | 13 |
| 14 | 15 | 16 | 17 | 18 | 19 | 20 |
| 21 | 22 | 23 | 24 | 25 | 26 | 27 |
| 28 | 29 | 30 | | | | |

**5** かんじ

What is the date and day of the week of your birthday this year? Complete the sentence below. Remember that the order of giving this date is month, date and day of the week.

ことし、誕生日（たんじょうび）は＿＿＿＿＿＿＿＿＿＿＿＿＿＿＿です。／でした。

## 6 かんじ

In an English class at Keio Shonan Fujisawa High School, these students wrote down three sentences about themselves. Write what they said in 日本語 using かんじ, ひらがな and カタカナ.

1 On Sunday, I sometimes go to town. In town, I hang out with my friends. I love shopping!

2 I'm a member of the basketball club. I love basketball. We practice on Monday, Wednesday, Friday and Saturday.

# パートA On the phone

## 7 かいてみよう

Here is a written version of what ふみえさん said when she phoned her friend あいさん. Use this as an example and write down a possible conversation for the people on the next page when they call their friends.

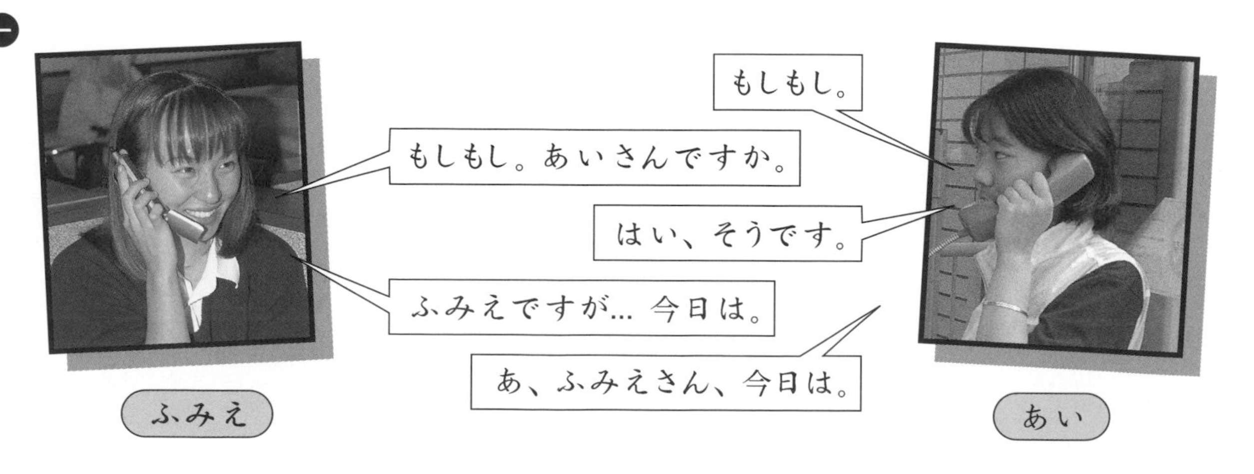

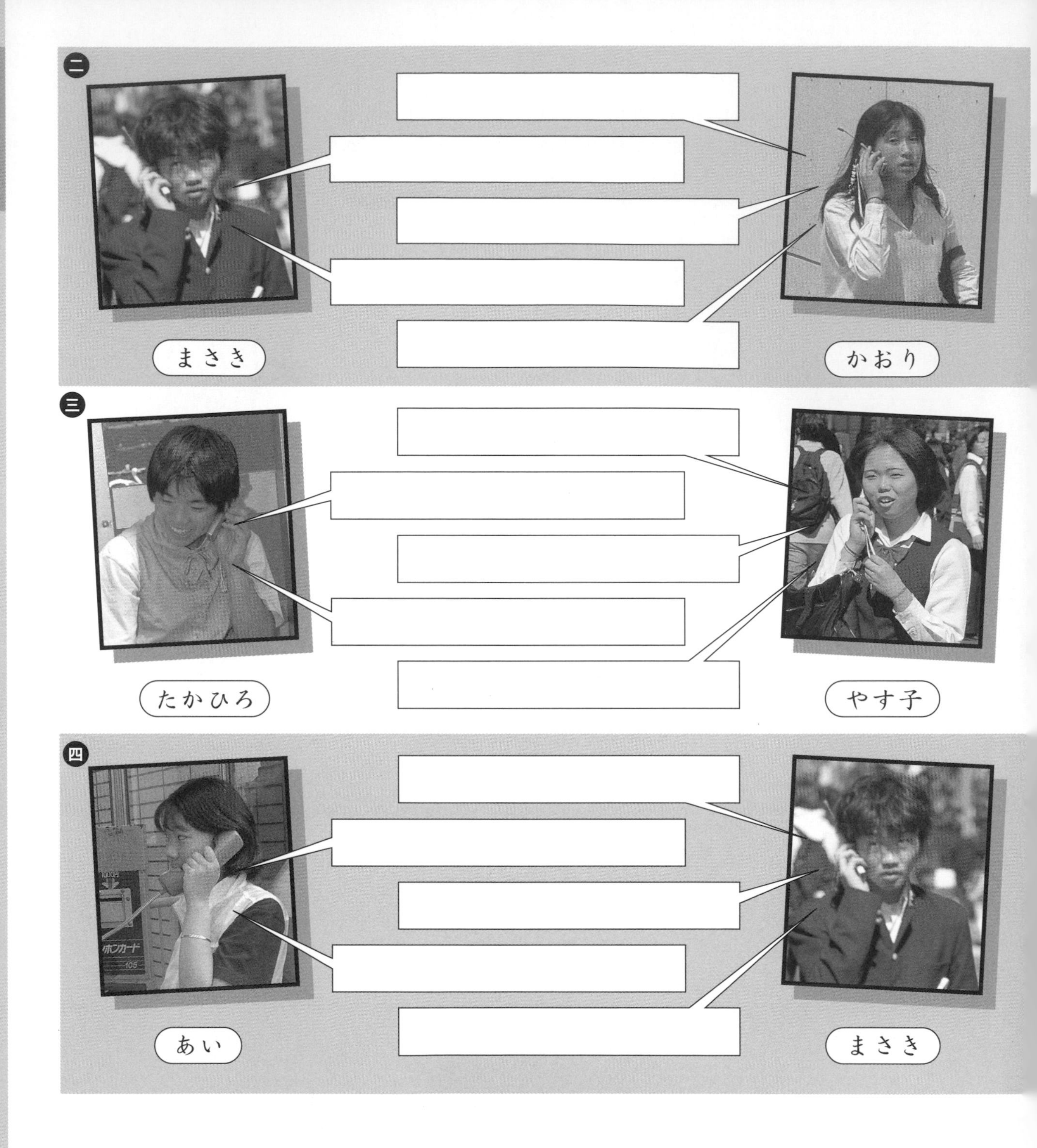


## 8 かいてみよう

Now write a statement about what the people above did. The first one has been done for you.

1 ふみえさんはあいさんにでんわをかけました。

2 ______________________________

3 ______________________________

4 ______________________________

## 9 かいてみよう

けいたいでんわ (mobile phones) are very popular because you can make and take calls from lots of places. Hidden below are 14 places where you could be when you hear 'rrring'. Highlight them in at least two colors.

## 10 きいてみようA

せいじくん is always on his phone! Listen to the start of some his calls as he asks his friends where they are. Write what they tell him in the space below their name.

一 かおり

二 がく

三 やす子

四 まみ

五 たかひろ

六 まさき

## 11 かいてみよう

Read about けいたいでんわ in おもしろい日本 on 80–81 ページ of your 今2 textbook and answer the following questions.

1 Which students really like having mobile phones?

Who do they call?

2 Some users of けいたいでんわ carry them around in their pockets. But where does すずさん keep hers?

3 When and how often does せいじくん ring his girlfriend?

Can you suggest why his phone bill is high?

4 If you have 'i-mode' on your phone, what kinds of things can you access?

5 What is being advertised in the final advertisement? How much are they? How many designs are available? What design do you prefer?

Invitations

## 12 かいてみよう

What have you been invited to do? When?

1 あした、かいものに行きませんか。

2 こんばん、いっしょにえいがを見ませんか。

3 日曜日のごご、サイクリングをしませんか。

4 土曜日のあさ、町に行きませんか。

5 今日はあついですね。プールに行きませんか。

6 金曜日のばん、いっしょにピッツァをたべませんか。

## 13 きいてみようB

It's the start of summer vacation and various people are inviting friends to do things. Listen as a group of people all accept invitations. Write the number of the conversation below the picture which best shows where they have been invited.

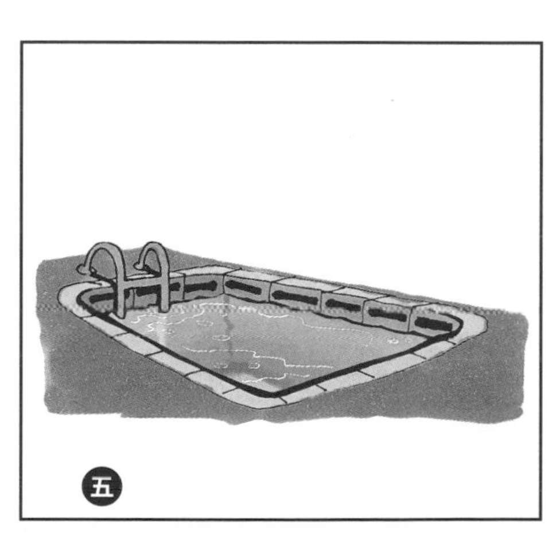


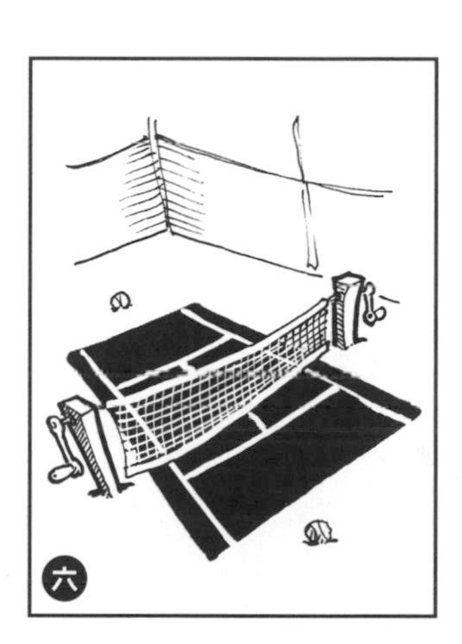


Now listen as people decline invitations. Check the box that best shows why they didn't accept.

1 ❑ place/activity not good ❑ time not good
2 ❑ place/activity not good ❑ time not good
3 ❑ place/activity not good ❑ time not good
4 ❑ place/activity not good ❑ time not good
5 ❑ place/activity not good ❑ time not good
6 ❑ place/activity not good ❑ time not good

## かいてみよう

がくくん is planning his weekend and he has invited ふみえさん and ひろしくん to go out. Here is what happened with each friend. Write the conversation that probably took place.

| |
|---|
| **1** He invited ふみえさん to the movies tonight. She accepted.<br>**2** He invited ひろしくん to a restaurant on Saturday night. Saturday was no good for ひろしくん so がくくん suggested Sunday night. ひろしくん accepted. |

**1** がくくん: ____________________
ふみえさん: ____________________

**2** がくくん: ____________________
ひろしくん: ____________________
がくくん: ____________________
ひろしくん: ____________________

## 15 かいてみよう

What will you say in the following situations? Choose from the list below. You can use some responses more than once.

| |
|---|
| あしたですか。　テニスはちょっと…　いいですね。<br>土曜日はちょっと…　じゃ、木曜日はどうですか。 |

**1** Someone that you really like has invited you out.

____________________

**2** Your friends want you to go shopping with them on Saturday but you are going out with your family.

____________________

**3** Your friend can't go swimming with you on Wednesday but she might be free another day...

____________________

**4** You're confirming that the invitation is for tomorrow.

____________________

**5** The person you really like has invited you out again!

____________________

**6** You've been invited to play tennis but you're not keen on tennis.

____________________

## 16 きいてみようC

せいじくん is still on the phone and he is inviting his friends to do things and go places with him. Unfortunately his friends are pretty busy and せいじくん has to suggest some other times, places or activities. He's managed to write down some new arrangements for himself, but would like you to listen to the conversations and write down as much information as you can about what they are going to do, and where and when they are going.

## 17 かいてみよう

ひろしくん likes くみ子さん and has sent her an email inviting her to do lots of things at various times over the weekend. She's really pleased and wants to go if she's free, but is too busy with 英語のしゅくだい to answer. Look at her diary with her weekend plans and write responses for her in the spaces given below.

送信者(そうしんしゃ)：くみ子 <kumi@hotmail.com>

宛先(あてさき)：ひろし <hiro@jiffy.ne.jp>

件名(けんめい)：しゅうまつ

日付(ひづけ)：7月15日

1 土曜日のあさ、いっしょにすいえいに行きませんか。

______________________________

2 土曜日のごご、いっしょにかいものに行きませんか。

______________________________

3 土曜日のばん、いっしょにレストランでたべませんか。

______________________________

4 日曜日のあさ、いっしょにジョッギングをしませんか。

______________________________

5 日曜日のごご、いっしょにフットボールを見ませんか。

______________________________

| | あさ | ごご | ばん |
|---|---|---|---|
| 土 | テニス | | えいが |
| 日 | | 町 | |

**18** よんでみよう

Look at the top of くみ子さん's email reply on the opposite page and see if you can guess what the following words mean. Draw a line to match each word to its English equivalent.

| | |
|---|---|
| 送信者（そうしんしゃ） | subject of message |
| 宛先（あてさき） | person who is sending the message |
| 件名（けんめい） | date of message |
| 日付（ひづけ） | person who will receive the message |

**19** Design an invitation to, say, a class restaurant outing, a birthday party, a farewell party, a barbeque...
You should include the kind of party, place, day and date, start and finish times, and a phone number for people to respond. You might like to have a theme and decorate your invitation accordingly.
Here are some headings that may be useful.

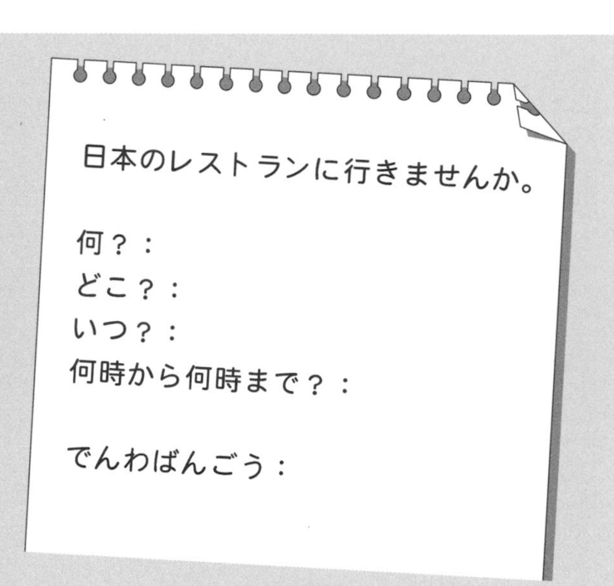


# パートC Putting it together

**20** In the photo story もしもし, which begins on 71 ページ of your 今2 textbook, how did people say these things?

**1** Where are you at the moment?

________________________________________

**2** Would you like to have lunch with me at McDonald's tomorrow?

________________________________________

**3** I like McDonald's. I like Fumie too.

________________________________________

**4** My friend Kumiko and I are going to McDonald's at 12.30.

________________________________________

5 I'm not crazy about burgers...what about some udon?

______________________________________________

6 Actually, I've got a tummy ache.

______________________________________________

7 Really? That's too bad. Kumiko is going too!

______________________________________________

8 I'll take some medicine tonight.

______________________________________________

## 21 よんでみよう

Read the photo story もしもし, which begins on 71 ページ of your 今2 textbook, and choose the correct answer from the alternatives given in each statement below.

**1**

| | | |
|---|---|---|
| ふみえさんは | くみ子さん<br>がくくん<br>ひろしくん | にでんわをかけます。 |

**2**

| | | |
|---|---|---|
| がくくんは、今、 | へや<br>うち<br>町 | にいます。 |

**3**

| | | |
|---|---|---|
| あした、ふみえさんは | マクドナルド<br>ケーエフシー<br>バーガーバー | でランチをたべます。 |

**4**

| | | |
|---|---|---|
| ひろしくんは | バーガー<br>うどん<br>くみ子さん | があまり好きじゃないです。 |

**5**

| | | |
|---|---|---|
| じつは、ひろしくんは | おなか<br>耳<br>せなか | がいたいんです。 |

**6**

| | | |
|---|---|---|
| あした、ふみえさんとくみ子さんは | がくくん<br>がくくんとひろしくん<br>ひろしくん | とランチをたべます。 |

## 22 きいてみようD

Use a highlighter to track the sequence of this conversation.

| もしもし。 | すずさん<br>けいくん | ですか。 |
|---|---|---|

| もしもし。はい、そうです。 |
|---|

| まきですが…。<br>たかですが…。 | 今、どこにいますか。 |
|---|---|

| 今、 | へや<br>としょかん<br>町 | にいます。ちょっとつまらないです。 |
|---|---|---|

| まきさん<br>たかくん | は？ |
|---|---|

| わたし<br>ぼく | は<br>も | へや<br>としょかん<br>町 | にいます。 |
|---|---|---|---|

| あのう、 | こんばん<br>あしたのばん<br>土曜日のばん | いっしょに | えいがを見ませんか。<br>ピッツァをたべませんか。<br>パーティーに行きませんか。 |
|---|---|---|---|

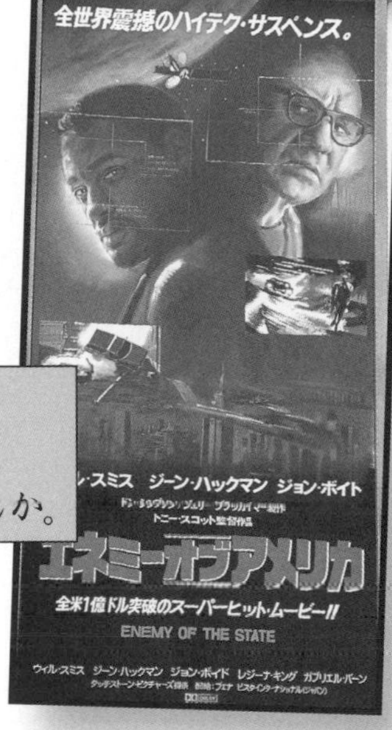


| えいが<br>ピッツァ<br>パーティー | ですか。 | えいが<br>ピッツァ<br>パーティー | はちょっと… |
|---|---|---|---|

| じつは | 目<br>おなか<br>耳<br>あし | がいたいんです。 |
|---|---|---|

| ああ、そうですか。ざんねんですね。 |
|---|

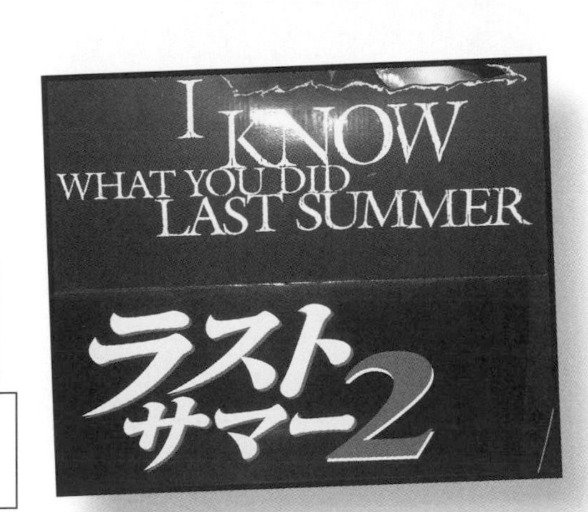


| じゃ、らいしゅうの | 金曜日<br>土曜日 | のばんはどうですか。 |
|---|---|---|

| らいしゅうの | 金曜日<br>土曜日 | のばんですか。いいですね。 |
|---|---|---|

| らいしゅう、また、でんわをかけます。 | じゃ、また。<br>バイバイ。 |
|---|---|

| じゃ、また。<br>バイバイ。 |
|---|

 A famous TV soap opera writer wants to sell his show *Heart-throb* to Japan and has asked you to write this scene in 日本語 based on the following brief. You may have to supply any information not detailed in the brief.

Brief for *Heart-throb*

- Boy rings girl and asks her out – he gives a time and a place.
- She's actually not well today so he suggests another time.
- The new time is fine but she isn't that keen on where he suggests they go.
- He suggests somewhere else.
- She enthusiastically accepts.
- He's really pleased and confirms the time.
- They say goodbye.

ドキドキ

## 24 きいてみようE

ひろ子さん likes talking. Listen to her conversations with various people and highlight what she is asking from the options given.

**1** She is asking トムくん:

- his age
- the time
- his grade in school
- his phone number

**2** She is asking ロビンさん:

- where she is
- what the matter is
- how she gets to school
- how she finds something

**3** She is asking マークくん if:

- he is hungry
- he is thirsty
- he has a sore throat
- he has a sore stomach

**4** She is asking ハナさん what kind of:

- films she likes
- salad she likes
- sports she plays
- music she listens to

**5** She is talking to リーくん and:

- invites him to go the pool
- suggests going to the pool
- asks him how the pool was
- asks if he has been to the pool

**6** She is asking アビーさん:

- her nationality
- where she was born
- where she lives now
- what language she speaks

**7** She is asking ジャックくん the price of:

- the tennis bag
- the tennis balls
- the tennis shoes
- the tennis racquet

**8** She is inviting you to a party on:

- Friday night
- Saturday night
- Sunday night
- Monday night

## 25 パズルあそび

Complete this クロスワードパズル in ひらがな.

### よこ→

2 ★町に行きませんか。

☆＿＿＿＿＿＿＿。行きましょう。

4 ★じゃ、えいが＿＿＿＿＿＿＿。

(how about... )

8 ★あしたのごごはちょっと...

☆じゃ、＿＿＿＿＿＿＿は どうですか。

★あしたのばんですか。いいですね。

10 ★バイバイ。

☆＿＿＿＿＿＿＿。

(See you tomorrow)

11 友だちに＿＿＿＿＿＿＿を かけました。

12 おみやげの＿＿＿＿＿＿＿で かいものをしましょう。

13 がくくんはひろしくんにでんわを

＿＿＿＿＿＿＿。

### たて↓

1 ＿＿＿＿＿＿＿、耳がいたいんです。

(Actually)

2 ★今、どこにいますか。

☆町に＿＿＿＿＿＿＿。

3 ぼくはマクドナルドもふみえさんも

＿＿＿＿＿＿＿です。

5 いっしょに＿＿＿＿＿＿＿ に行きませんか。

6 ＿＿＿＿＿＿＿。がくくんですか。 ふみえですが...

7 こんばんですか。＿＿＿＿＿＿＿ はちょっと...

9 今日、いっしょにえいがを

＿＿＿＿＿＿＿。

11 もしもし。ひろし＿＿＿＿＿＿＿...

## 1 かんじ

Practice writing these new かんじ.

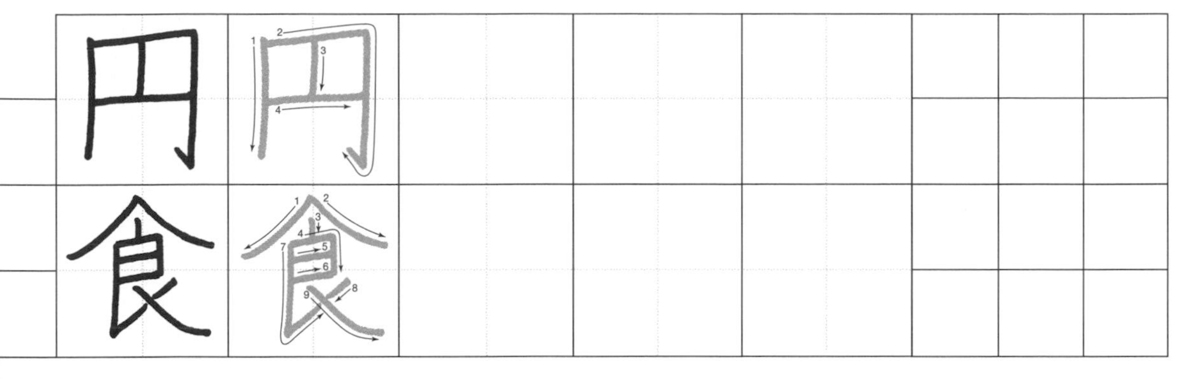


## 2 かんじ

Often in small レストラン in Japan, the menu with the names and prices of dishes is written on paper and hung on the wall. Write a レストランのメニュー by filling in the blank signs below with the following list of food items. Since these signs are in たてがき, you will need to write the prices in かんじ. The first one has been done for you. (You can see pictures of some of these dishes on 98–99 ページ of your textbook.)

| | | | | | | | |
|---|---|---|---|---|---|---|---|
| みそしる | ¥200 | ぎょうざ | ¥300 | うどん | ¥350 | ラーメン | ¥390 |
| かつどん | ¥700 | カレーライス | ¥600 | そば | ¥400 | | |

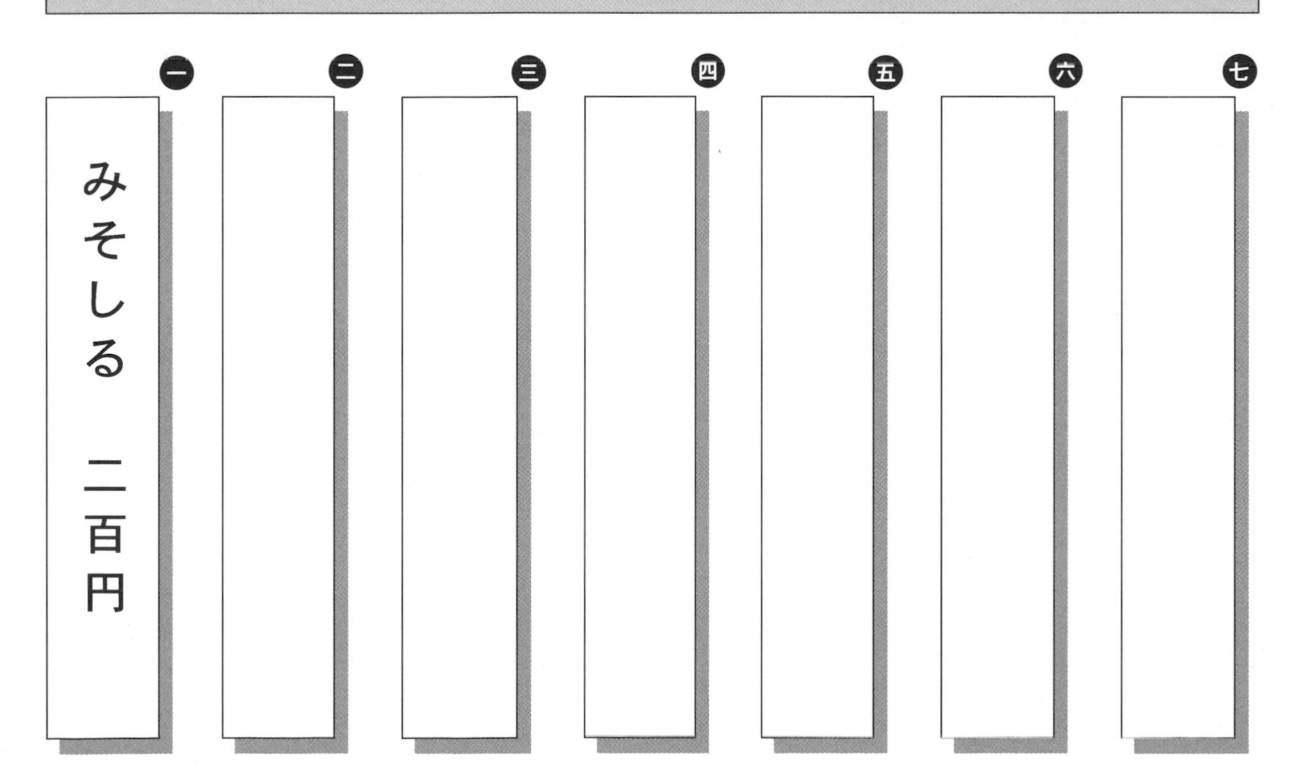

**3** かんじ

In the かいてみよう section of your textbook, you have seen lots of mnemonics – these are the little pictures that sometimes help you to remember the かんじ. Some mnemonics for 食 show a bowl of cooked rice resting on a stand with a lid, others show a picture of a parfait dessert with a little umbrella on top. What works for you? Try drawing your own mnemonics for 食 and 円.

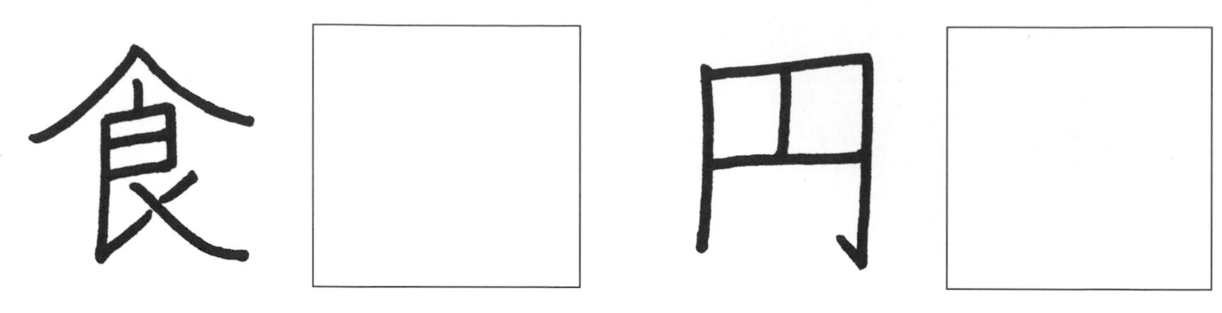


**4** かんじ

In the space following each of the words below, write 食べます if you can eat it, 行きます if you can go to it, or 人 if it is a person.

ハンバーガー（　　　　　）　学校（　　　　　）　友だち（　　　　　）

町（　　　　　）　ドーナツ（　　　　　）　お母さん（　　　　　）

オーストラリア人（　　　　　）　おべんとう（　　　　　）

ホットドッグ（　　　　　）　レストラン（　　　　　）

**5** かんじ

Answer these 'food' questions in sentences using ひらがな, カタカナ and かんじ.

**1** あさごはんにトーストを食べますか。

______________________________

**2** 学校で何時にランチを食べますか。

______________________________

**3** ファーストフードが好きですか、ヘルシーフードが好きですか。

______________________________

何を食べますか。

______________________________

**4** いちばん好きな食べものは何ですか。（食べもの　food）

______________________________

# パートA

**Deciding what to have**

**6** かいてみよう

しょうじくん and his friends have decided to have the following drinks. Write the name of the person under the drink they are having. Then write labels for the drinks.

1 きみひろくんはシェーキにします。
2 さちよさんはオレンジジュースにします。
3 あきなさんはコーラにします。
4 ゆりさんはコーヒーにします。
5 たかひろくんもコーヒーにします。
6 サイモンくんは シェーキにします。
7 ケーティーさんはオレンジジュースにします。
8 しょうじくんはカプチーノにします。

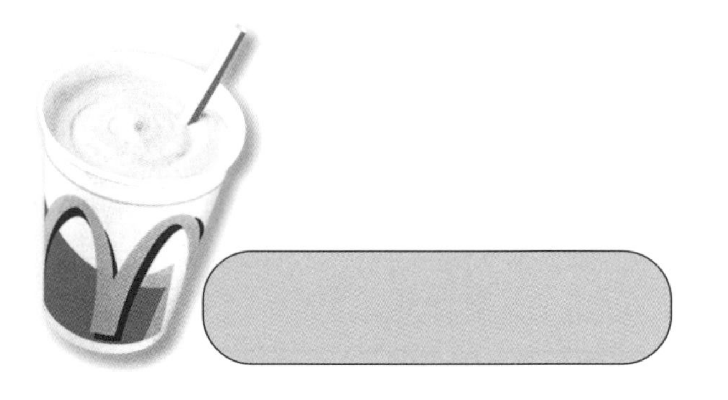

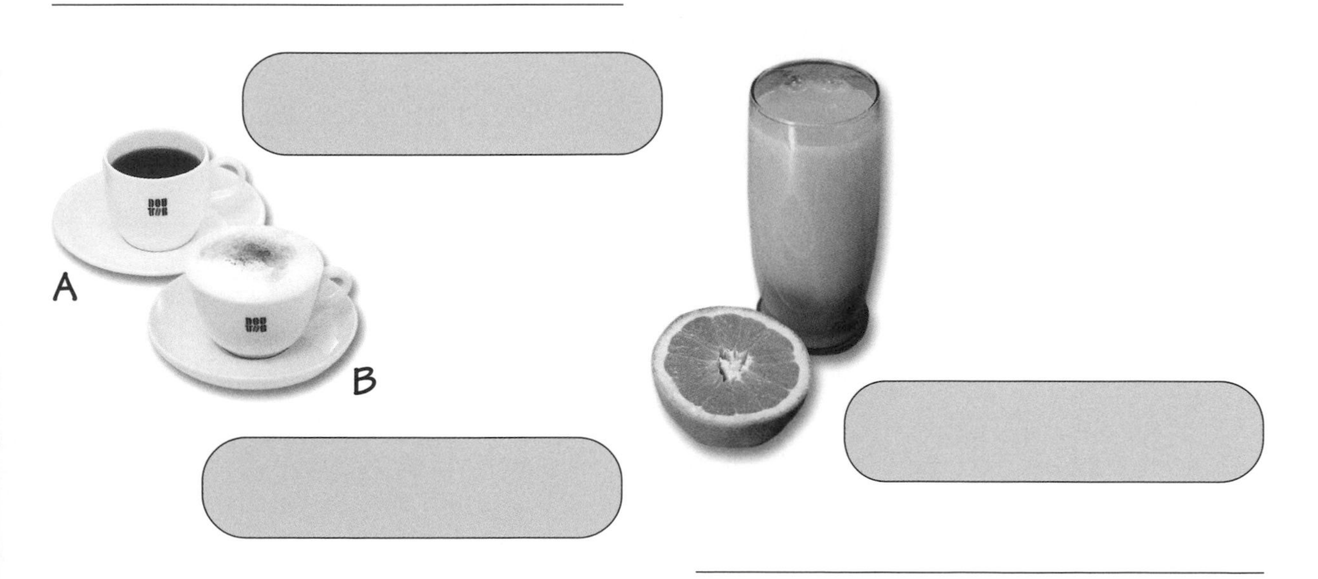

A

B

A

B

## 7 かいてみよう

These people are all deciding what to have. You can see where they are heading by their selections in this picture. Write down their responses to the question 何にしますか in the space below.

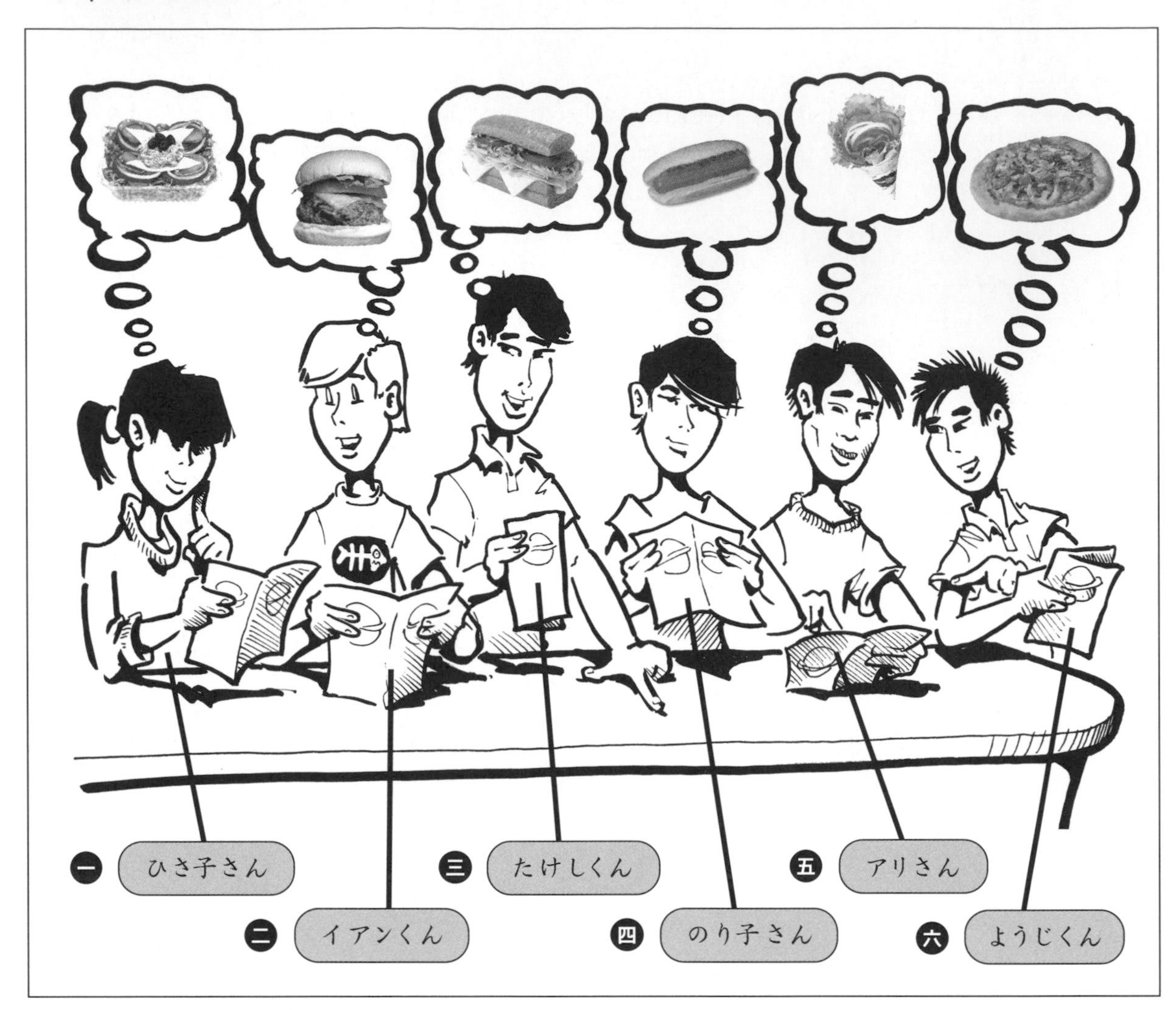


1 ひさ子さん、何にしますか。

______________________________

2 イアンくん、何にしますか。

______________________________

3 たけしくん、何にしますか。

______________________________

4 のり子さん、何にしますか。

______________________________

5 アリさん、何にしますか。

______________________________

6 ようじくん、何にしますか。

______________________________

# パートB

Counting various things
Ordering a meal

8 かいてみよう

Write the correct 〜つ number in かんじ and ひらがな under each group of items. Then complete the blank square with a food item and a 〜つ number that has not been used.

一

二

三

四

五

六

七

八

CHIPS

九

十

## 9 きいてみようA

How about two quick games of ビンゴ using the ～つ numbers? Write down two sets of five numbers between one and ten inclusive in the grid below and listen for your numbers! (Check with せん生 to see what fabulous prizes are available...)

| ゲーム 1 | | | | | |
|---|---|---|---|---|---|
| ゲーム 2 | | | | | |

## 10 きいてみようB

あき子さん is doing some odd shopping around town. The pictures below show what she bought. Write in the space how many of each thing she bought.

⑪ 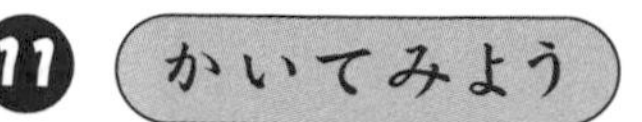


Your class is going to アモーレレストラン. The レストラン has sent you the メニュー in advance and everyone has marked on it what they want to have. Your task is to collate everyone's デザート order and write it out neatly so that it can be given to the chef when you arrive. Here is the information – せん生 has done the first one for you so that you know what to do.

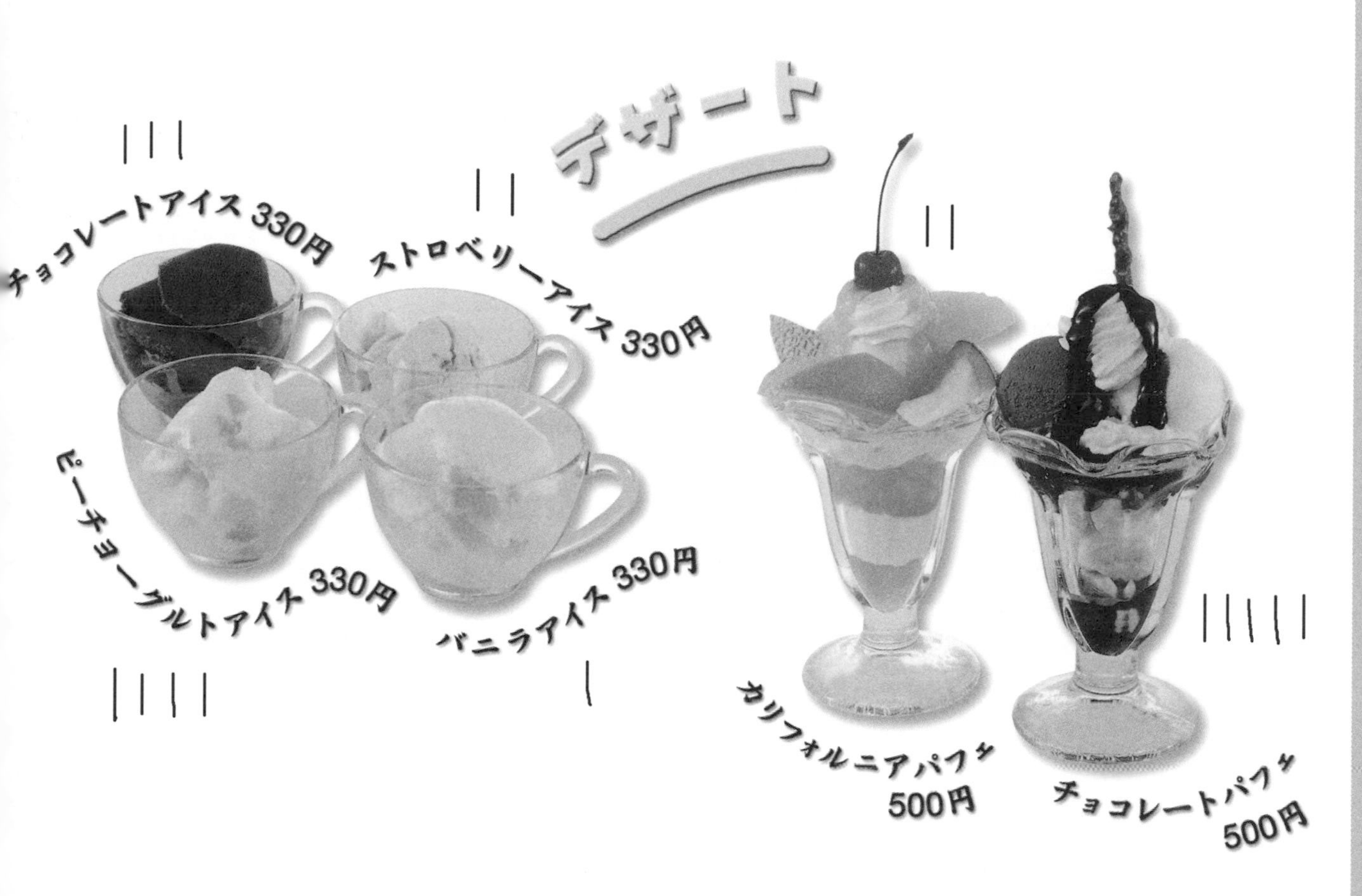


1 チョコレートアイスをみっつください。

2 ______

3 ______

4 ______

5 ______

6 ______

第四課

**12** かいてみよう

You are applying for a part-time job in a Japanese fast food restaurant. Here is part of the written test. You can practice here before the actual test by answering these questions.

**1** What do you say to welcome the customer?

______________________________

**2** How do you ask someone for their order?

______________________________

**3** How do you find out if they would like a drink?

______________________________

4 How do you ask about their dessert order?

______________________________

**5** If someone orders 2 burgers and 1 cola, how would you confirm or repeat back their order?

______________________________

______________________________

**13** You also need to be able to understand what the customer（おきゃくさん）says to you! Complete the next part of the test by explaining what has happened in the following situations.

**1** おきゃくさん：チキンバーガーを三つ、おねがいします。

______________________________

**2** おきゃくさん：コーヒーをください。

______________________________

**3** おきゃくさん：デザートですか。デザートはけっこうです。

______________________________

**4** おきゃくさん：そのセットはいくらですか。

______________________________

## 14 きいてみようC

You are doing some research about what kinds of foods young Japanese people eat for lunch. You've decided to sit in a popular restaurant and listen as several groups give their orders. Record their orders on the menu sheet below by writing how many of each item they decide to have.

| | グループ 1 | グループ 2 | グループ 3 | グループ 4 | グループ 5 | グループ 6 |
|---|---|---|---|---|---|---|
| カツカレー | | | | | | |
| ハムサンド | | | | | | |
| すしセット | | | | | | |
| おべんとう | | | | | | |
| アイスクリーム | | | | | | |
| チョコレートパフェ | | | | | | |
| コーラ | | | | | | |
| メロンソーダ | | | | | | |
| ミネラルウォーター | | | | | | |

## 15 かいてみよう

Here are pictures showing what people have ordered. Use them to complete these restaurant dialogues between the customer（おきゃくさん）and the waiter（ウェーター）.

1 ウェーター：　いらっしゃいませ。ごちゅうもんは？

おきゃくさん：______________________________

______________________________

ウェーター：　おのみものは？

おきゃくさん：______________________________

ウェーター：　チキンカツバーガーを二つと、フライドポテトを一つと、コーラを一つですね。

2 ウェーター：　いらっしゃいませ。ごちゅうもんは？

おきゃくさん：______________________________

______________________________

ウェーター：　________________？

おきゃくさん：______________________________

ウェーター：　______________________________

______________________________

**3** ウェーター： いらっしゃいませ。＿＿＿＿＿＿＿＿＿＿？

おきゃくさん：＿＿＿＿＿＿＿＿＿＿＿＿＿＿＿＿＿＿＿＿＿＿＿＿＿＿＿＿＿＿

＿＿＿＿＿＿＿＿＿＿＿＿＿＿＿＿＿＿＿＿＿＿＿＿＿＿＿＿＿＿

ウェーター： ＿＿＿＿＿＿＿＿＿＿？

おきゃくさん：＿＿＿＿＿＿＿＿＿＿＿＿＿＿＿＿＿＿＿＿＿＿＿＿＿＿＿＿＿＿

ウェーター： ＿＿＿＿＿＿＿＿＿＿＿＿＿＿＿＿＿＿＿＿＿＿＿＿＿＿＿＿＿＿

＿＿＿＿＿＿＿＿＿＿＿＿＿＿＿＿＿＿＿＿＿＿＿＿＿＿＿＿＿＿

**4** ウェーター： ＿＿＿＿＿＿＿＿＿＿。＿＿＿＿＿＿＿＿＿＿？

おきゃくさん：＿＿＿＿＿＿＿＿＿＿＿＿＿＿＿＿＿＿＿＿＿＿＿＿＿＿＿＿＿＿

＿＿＿＿＿＿＿＿＿＿＿＿＿＿＿＿＿＿＿＿＿＿＿＿＿＿＿＿＿＿

ウェーター： ＿＿＿＿＿＿＿＿＿＿？

おきゃくさん：＿＿＿＿＿＿＿＿＿＿＿＿＿＿＿＿＿＿＿＿＿＿＿＿＿＿＿＿＿＿

ウェーター： ＿＿＿＿＿＿＿＿＿＿＿＿＿＿＿＿＿＿＿＿＿＿＿＿＿＿＿＿＿＿

＿＿＿＿＿＿＿＿＿＿＿＿＿＿＿＿＿＿＿＿＿＿＿＿＿＿＿＿＿＿

# パートC Putting it together

**16** かいてみよう

Read the photo story 4人で which starts on 83ページ of your 今2 textbook and answer the following questions.

1 Where have the boys met ?

2 What have the friends of がくくん and ひろしくん invited them to do?

3 What are がくくん and ひろしくん going to do?

4 Why does がくくん seem annoyed with ひろしくん?

5 What is がくくん being teased about?

6 What does がくくん get for lunch? How much is it?

7 What happens when the girls and boys initially spot each other?

8 Trouble appears in the form of the friends of がくくん and ひろしくん. Explain what happens.

9 How does ふみえさん rescue the outing?

10 What do がくくん and ひろしくん do before they join the girls?

11 Can you suggest why the title of this story is 4人で?

**17** よんでみよう

Read the photo story 4人で which starts on 83ページ of your 今2 textbook and complete each statement by adding a verb.

1 がくくんとひろしくんはえきで友だちに ＿＿＿＿＿＿＿＿＿＿ 。

2 今から、がくくんとひろしくんはふみえさんとくみ子さんと
マクドナルドに行って、ランチを ＿＿＿＿＿＿＿＿＿＿ 。

3 がくくんはランチにチキンカツバーガーを ＿＿＿＿＿＿＿＿＿＿ 。

4 がくくんはふみえさんを見ます。ふみえさんはあそこに ＿＿＿＿＿＿＿＿＿＿ 。

5 がくくんとひろしくんはフライドポテトを三つ ＿＿＿＿＿＿＿＿＿＿ 。

6 がくくんとひろしくんの友だちもマクドナルドでランチを ＿＿＿＿＿＿＿＿＿＿ 。

7 ふみえさんはがくくんにでんわを ＿＿＿＿＿＿＿＿＿＿ 。

8 これから、がくくんとひろしくんはふみえさんとくみ子さんと
えいがを ＿＿＿＿＿＿＿＿＿＿ 。

**18** かいてみよう

がくくん's friend, だいすけくん, teased him and ひろしくん by saying:

ふみえさんとくみ子さんはあそこにいますよ。
がくくんとひろしくんはここにいます。

Explain だいすけくん's comments by drawing a floor plan to show where everyone is.

## 19 かいてみよう

How did you do with the みんなで role-play of the restaurant visit? Write a report of your role-play as if you and your friend actually visited the restaurant.
Here is an example written by David.

なまえ：デービッド

### アモーレレストランのレポート

せんしゅう、サムさんとアモーレレストランに行きました。
シーフードフライはおいしそうでした。だから、
ぼくはシーフードフライにしました。880円でした。
サムさんはミートソーススパゲッティにしました。
それもおいしそうでした。それは680円でした。
ぼくもサムさんもキャロットジュースにしました。
キャロットジュースは300円でした。
ぼくはシーフードフライを一つと、ミートソーススパゲッティを
一つと、キャロットジュースをちゅうもんしました。
デザートはバニラアイスでした。いっしょに食べました。とても
おいしかったです。アモーレレストランはよかったです。
また行きます。

ちゅうもんしました　ordered

## 20 きいてみようD

Decide what is happening in these short conversations, recorded in a restaurant. Highlight your answer from the options given.

**1** He is:
- ordering a pizza
- deciding what to have
- commenting on the food

**2** She is:
- taking an order
- asking the price
- welcoming customers

**3** He is:
- taking an order
- ordering a drink
- welcoming customers

**4** She is:
- ordering a drink
- ordering some food
- commenting on the food

**5** He is:
- taking an order
- ordering a drink
- deciding what to have

**6** They are:
- ordering their meal
- deciding what to have
- commenting on the food

## 21 かいてみよう

In おもしろい日本 on 98–99ページ of your 今2 textbook, ひろしくん talks about 日本りょうり. Read his しょうかい and then answer the following questions.

**1** What does ひろしくん like doing sometimes on Sunday?

______________________________

**2** ひろしくん has described a couple of かつ dishes. What is a かつ? You have also seen かつ used in foods like カツカレー and チキンカツバーガー. Can you suggest why かつ is written in カタカナ in these foods?

______________________________

______________________________

**3** Name the three types of noodles that are popular in 日本 and also with ひろしくん.

______________________________

**4** Have you eaten any of the dishes that ひろしくん describes?

______________________________

5 Have you eaten any other 日本りょうり?

6 Looking at the pictures, which do you think that you would like to try?

7 Is the dish that you have chosen やすい or たかい?

8 How would you order it in 日本語?

9 Of course, there are many dishes that ひろしくん has not mentioned in his introduction to 日本りょうり.

For example:

- やきとり
- すきやき
- てんぷら
- うなぎ
- かまめし
- さしみ
- おこのみやき
- しゃぶしゃぶ
- ふぐ

Find out about some of these and present your findings to your class. You can start at your library or ask some Japanese friends.

You could also use the Internet to find out more about 日本りょうり. Here are a couple of website addresses that may be helpful.

http://bento.com

## 22 パズルあそび

Complete these series of words.

1 ひとつ　みっつ　いつつ　________

2 みっつ　むっつ　よっつ　________

3 ひとつ　ひとり　________　ふたり

4 いつか　いつつ　ここのか　________

5 みっつ　みっか　よっつ　________

## 23 パズルあそび

Which person is being talked about? Complete the puzzle by writing the sentences in ひらがな, カタカナ and かんじ and the answer will appear in the shaded boxes.

1 The restaurant is over there.

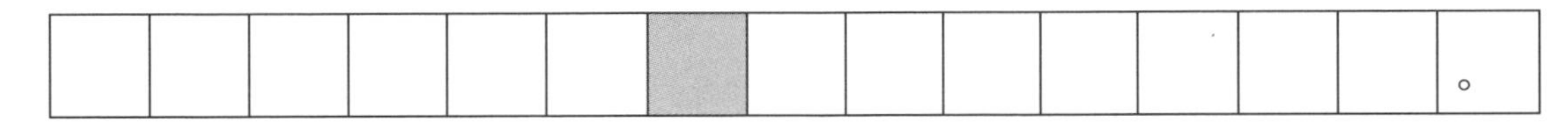

2 Mr. Hirano is here.

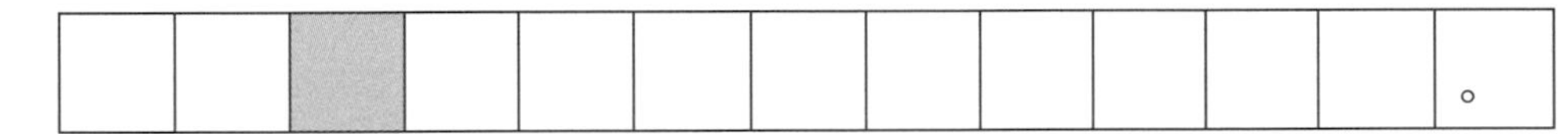

3 Hiroshi likes udon, doesn't he?

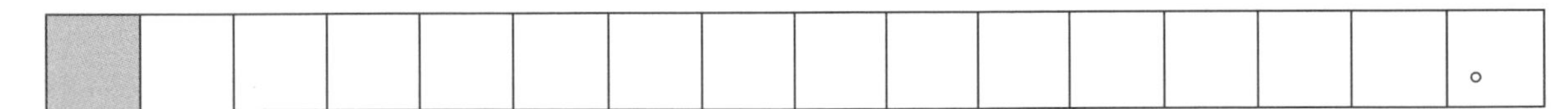

4 I'll have an obento please.

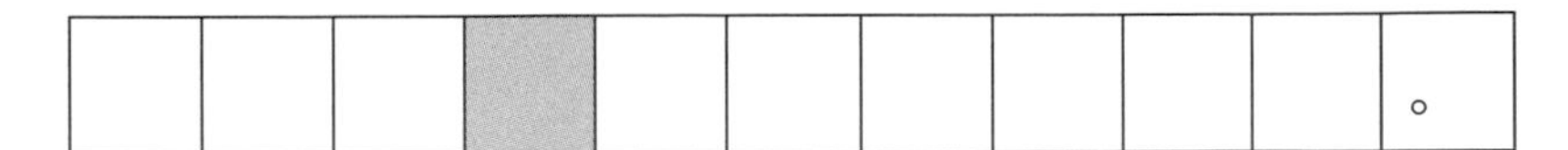

5 Juice is ¥300.

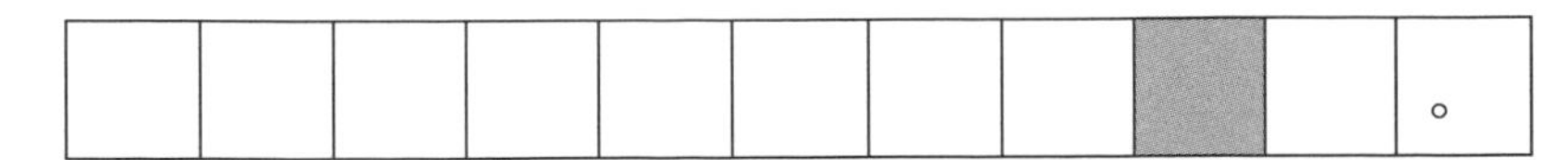

6 The sushi looks good.

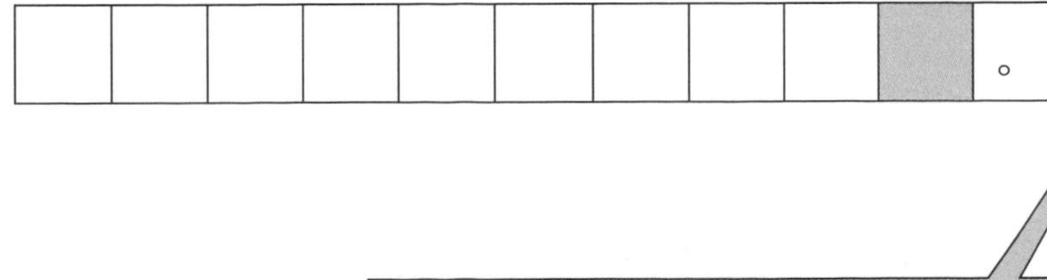

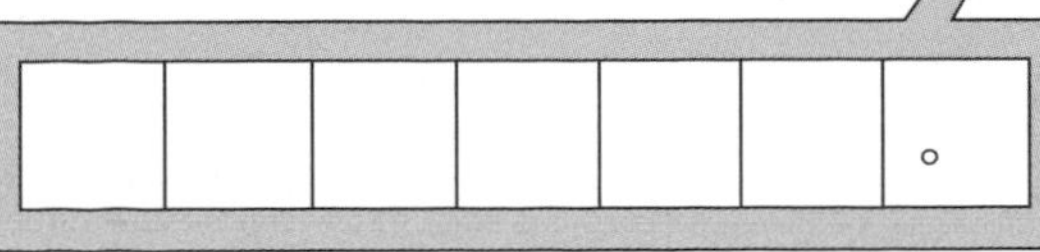

# 第五課

## 1 かんじ

Practice writing these new かんじ.

| | | | | | | | | |
|---|---|---|---|---|---|---|---|---|
| | 山 | 山 | | | | | | |
| | 川 | 川 | | | | | | |
| | 田 | 田 | | | | | | |

## しってる？

- 山 (やま) is used to refer to mountains in general. It is also used after the name of a mountain to mean Mt.～. When it means Mt.～, the reading of 山 is ～さん. Mt. Fuji, Japan's highest mountain, is called ふじさん(富士山).
  川 is also used for the name of rivers. It changes to がわ when it follows a river's name. For example, the river flowing through Tokyo is called すみだがわ (隅田川).
  Can you give, in 日本語, the name of a river and mountain near where you live?

  __________________________ __________________________

- 田（た）and 口（くち） are commonly used in family names and places.
  Their readings change to だ and ぐち when they are not the first かんじ.
  For example: 本田→ほんだ　水口→みずぐち　隅田川→すみだがわ

## 2 かんじ

Here are some めいし (name cards). Who do they belong to?
Write the name of the person in ひらがな in the box near their めいし.

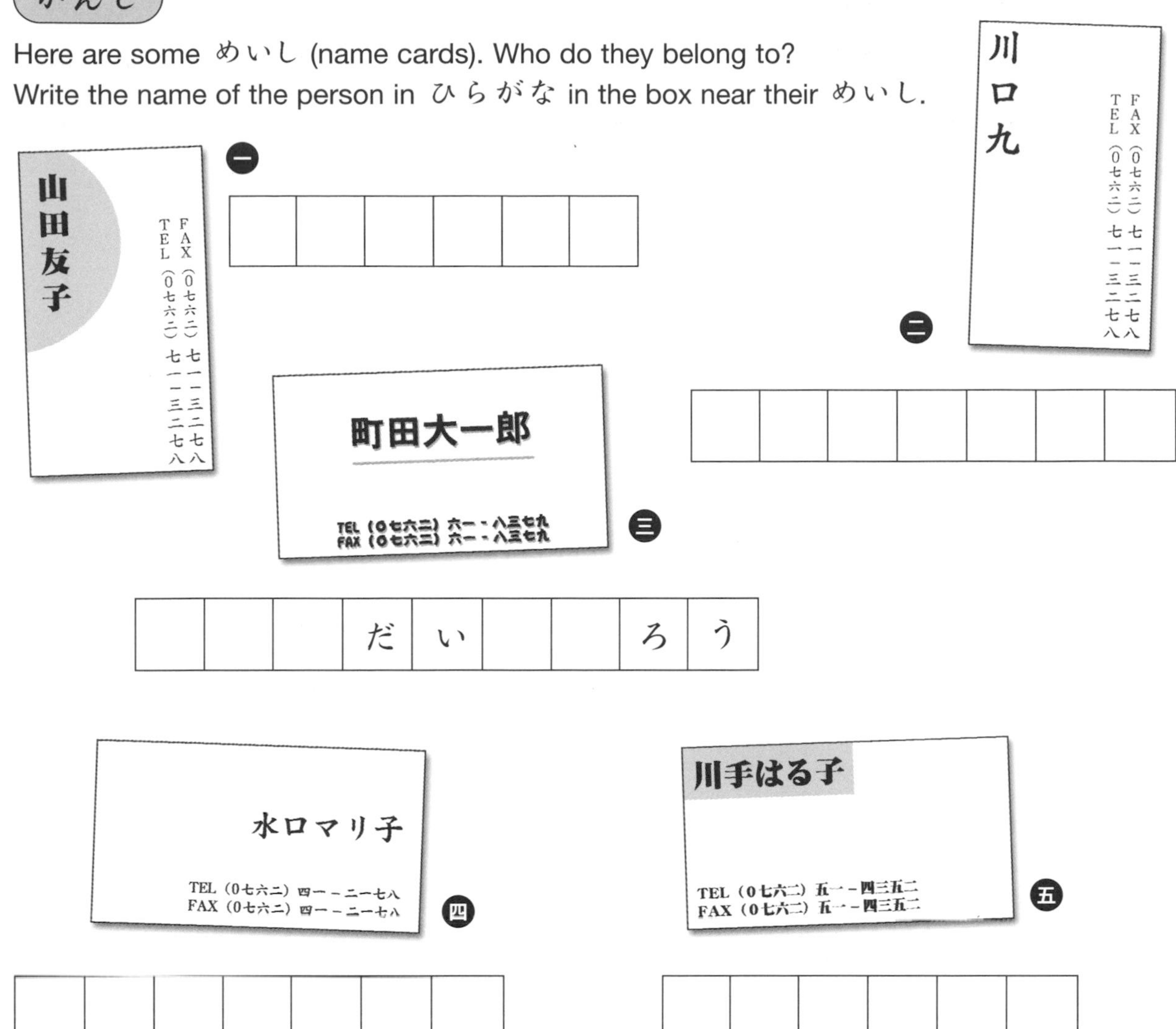


## 3 かんじ

As you know, many かんじ developed from pictures. Test how many of these you remember by writing each of the ひらがな below in かんじ and drawing a picture to show its 'history'. The first one has been done for you.

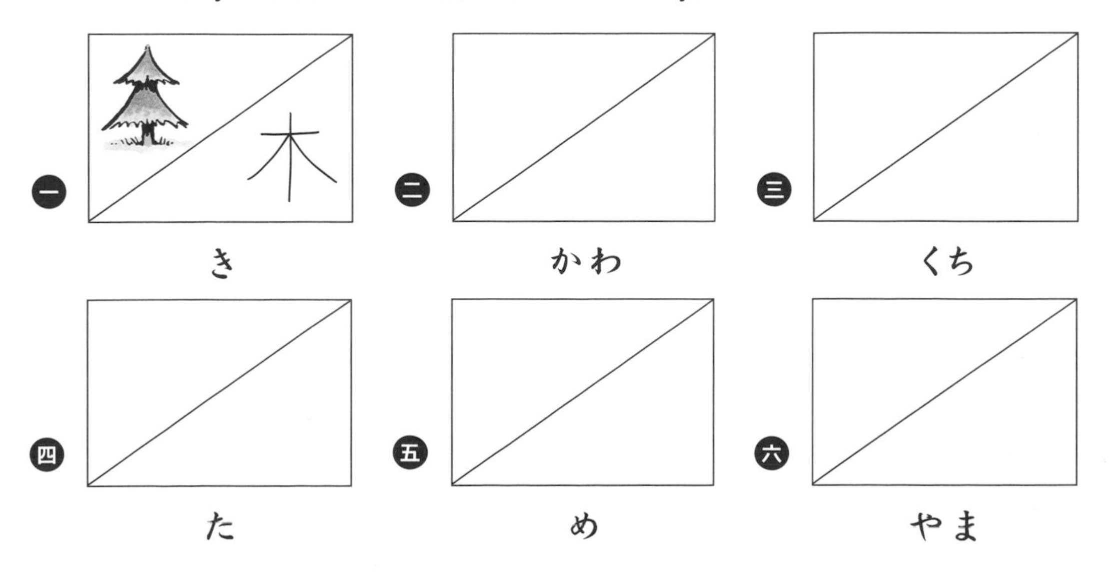

## 4 かんじ

You have previously seen how some かんじ are used to make up parts of new かんじ. Sometimes this can give a clue about the meaning of the new かんじ.
For example, we can see 日 which means *sun* used in 時 to mean *o'clock* or *time*. Can you suggest a connection?
Here are some かんじ which are used in other かんじ that you know. Write the かんじ and try to think of a connection for each.

1 日 ____________
〜よう (eg げつようび)

2 田 ____________ ____________
まち おとこ

3 口 ____________ ____________
〜ご (eg にほんご) なん？なに？

4 目 ____________
みます

# パートA

What's there? Who's there?
What's nearby?

## 5 かいてみよう

まさるくん is looking around his room and out of his window. Complete the following sentences about who or what is around him with います or あります.

1 へやにコンピューターが ____________。

2 へやにベッドが ____________。

3 へやにねこが ____________。

4 へやにテレビが ____________。

5 にわに木が ____________。

6 にわに父が ____________。

7 にわにいぬが ____________。

## 6 かいてみよう

ニコールさん, like you, is learning 日本語 and she has handed in the following homework. She wrote what there is in her town, school, house and room. Jot down in English what she wrote. Now write four similar sentences describing what is in your town, school, house and room. Try to make your sentences even more interesting than ニコールさん's.

なまえ：ニコール

1 わたしの町に大きいスーパーがあります。

2 学校にいいテニスコートがたくさんあります。

3 うちにあたらしいビリヤードテーブルがあります。

4 わたしのへやにふるいテレビがあります。

**In Nicole's**

town –

school –

house –

room –

1 ____________________

2 ____________________

3 ____________________

4 ____________________

## 7 きいてみようA

Things are really crowded today – it must be a holiday. Listen to these people comment and write the number of the conversation in the appropriate box.

**8** かいてみよう

ベンくん looked at this photo of ディズニーランド and wrote the comment you can see beneath it. Look at the pictures of crowded places on the opposite page and write a couple of sentences about each of them. Comment on the crowd and perhaps say why it is crowded.

こんでいますね。
ディズニーランドに学生がたくさんいます。

一 えいがかん ______________________

______________________

二 でんしゃ ______________________

______________________

三 こうえん ______________________

______________________

四 スーパー ______________________

______________________

五 CD のみせ ______________________

______________________

六 プール ______________________

______________________

## 9 かいてみよう

Look at the pictures of the food stands below and write what is there. The first one has been done for you.

## 10 きいてみようB

いま

Everyone got really hungry and thirsty at the 日光（にっこう） festival. Listen as they decide what food and drinks to have. Show that you can understand what they are talking about by writing the number of the conversation next to the appropriate stall.

バナナチョコ

二

ここにクレープがあります。

## ⑪ きいてみようC

Use a highlighter to track the sequence of this conversation.

| じゅん子さん<br>しゅんごくん | の | 町<br>うち<br>へや | はどんな | 町<br>うち<br>へや | ですか。 |
|---|---|---|---|---|---|

| 町<br>うち<br>へや | ですか。そうですね。 | わたし<br>ぼく | の | 町<br>うち<br>へや | は | きれい<br>きたない<br>大きい<br>ちいさい | です。 |
|---|---|---|---|---|---|---|---|

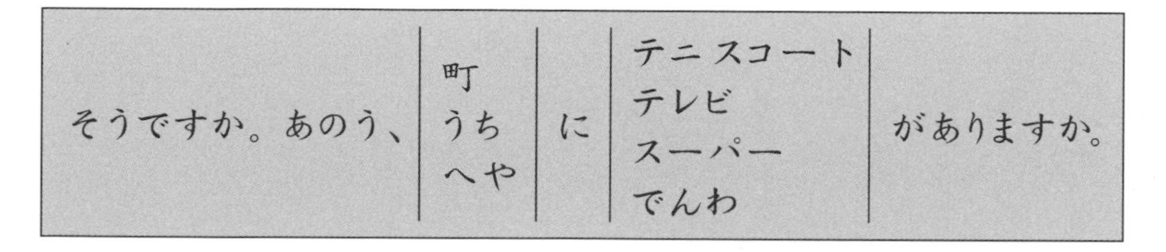

| そうですか。あのう、 | 町<br>うち<br>へや | に | テニスコート<br>テレビ<br>スーパー<br>でんわ | がありますか。 |
|---|---|---|---|---|

| ええ、あります。<br>いいえ、ありません。 | しょうこさん<br>たかのりくん | の | 町<br>うち<br>へや | には？ |
|---|---|---|---|---|

| わたし<br>ぼく | の | 町<br>うち<br>へや | には | テニスコート<br>プール<br>レストラン<br>コンピューター | がありますよ。 |
|---|---|---|---|---|---|

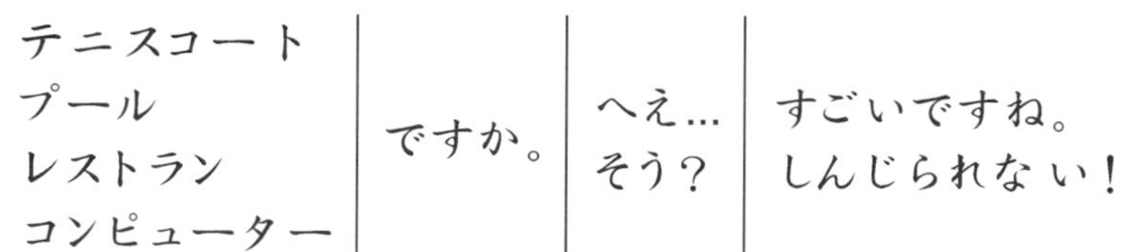

| テニスコート<br>プール<br>レストラン<br>コンピューター | ですか。 | へえ…<br>そう？ | すごいですね。<br>しんじられない！ |
|---|---|---|---|

## 12 かいてみよう

Look at the picture showing where けんじくん lives. For each of the following statements, mark ○（まる）if it is true and ✕（ばつ）if it is false.

1 けんじくんのうちのそばにこうえんがあります。 ○ ✕

2 けんじくんのうちのそばにスーパーがあります。 ○ ✕

3 けんじくんのうちのまえに田んぼがあります。 ○ ✕

4 けんじくんのうちのまえにえいがかんがあります。 ○ ✕

5 えいがかんのまえに学生がいます。 ○ ✕

6 レストランのまえにも学生がいます。 ○ ✕

7 けんじくんはへやにいます。 ○ ✕

8 へやにコンピューターがあります。 ○ ✕

9 へやにねこがいます。 ○ ✕

10 けんじくんのへやのまえににわがあります。 ○ ✕

11 にわにお母さんがいます。 ○ ✕

12 にわに木と川があります。 ○ ✕

13 けんじくんのうちは町にあります。 ○ ✕

## 13 かいてみよう

Answer the following questions about えみさんのうち.

1 えみさんのうちのそばに何がありますか。

---

2 えみさんのうちのまえに何がありますか。

---

3 えみさんのうちのまえにだれがいますか。

---

4 えみさんはへやにいますか。

---

5 えみさんのへやに何がありますか。

---

6 えみさんのへやにねこがいますか。

---

7 えみさんのうちはどんなうちですか。

---

## 14 かいてみよう

どんなうちですか。What is your house like? What is nearby? Answer the following questions about your house.

1 うちはどこにありますか。

___

2 あたらしいうちですか、ふるいうちですか。

___

3 うちは大きいですか、ちいさいですか。

___

4 にわがありますか。

___

5 (If はい) どんなにわですか。きれいなにわですか、大きいにわですか。

___

6 うちのそばに何がありますか。

___

7 うちのまえに何がありますか。

___

8 今のうちが好きですか。

___

Draw a map of your house and its surroundings and label as much as you can in 日本語.

## 15 かいてみよう

Write a real estate advertisement describing the appearance and location of each of these houses. You can say if it is big or small, old or new, if the garden is nice, if there are shops, schools or parks nearby (you can take a bit of licence here!) and what is nearby or in front of it. And, of course, they are all attractive homes!

三

| はし | bridge |
|---|---|

16 きいてみようD

Listen as 友子さん reads to you a description of the area around where she lives. Complete the sketch of the scene as she talks about it.

# パートB

What things do you have?

17 きいてみようE

A research company is checking out what kinds of things teenagers in Japan have in their rooms. They'd like you to fill in the survey form below as the teenagers give their answers. (Thank you for your co-operation.)

| | (TV) | (video recorder) | (telephone) | (CDs) | (computer) |
|---|---|---|---|---|---|
| 1 あつ子 | | | | | |
| 2 おさむ | | | | | |
| 3 こうじ | | | | | |
| 4 えり子 | | | | | |
| 5 りえ子 | | | | | |
| 6 けんたろう | | | | | |

**18** What would your 'dream room' be like? Write a description of what you would have in it and draw a plan. You could display your work (with your name hidden) around the classroom and try to match each 'dream room' with its 'dreamer'.

**19** きいてみようF

Jason is being interviewed about his house and his room for a Japanese student magazine. The reporter has asked you to jot down the essential facts so that you'll be able to check the article for her later. Use the note-pad sheet provided below. She has written in the location already.

**Jason's House**

location: *Canberra*

size:

number of rooms:

garden?:

nearby features:

**Jason's Room**

size:

facilities/'stuff'?:

# パートC

**At the festival**
**Putting it together**

## 20 きいてみようG

たかひろくん enjoys talking about the people at the 日光(にっこう)のまつり. Listen to his comments and write the number of the conversation next to the appropriate photo.

☐

☐

☐

☐

## 21 かいてみよう

山田たかひろくん talks about the location and attractions of 日光(にっこう) in frames 一 and 二 on 103 ページ of your textbook. The tourist association would like you to write some of this information in English so that they can include it in their brochures for overseas tourists.

_______________________________________________

_______________________________________________

_______________________________________________

_______________________________________________

_______________________________________________

_______________________________________________

_______________________________________________

**22** かいてみよう

「ぼくのかぞく(と友だち)はまつりが好きです。」
山田たかひろくん made this comment about his family and friends' involvement in the 日光(にっこう)のまつり. Write who he is referring to in the spaces below. Try to write at least five people.

______________ ______________ ______________

______________ ______________ ______________

**23** かいてみよう

山田たかひろくんはどんな人ですか。Complete these sentences that tell us a bit about him.

1 山田たかひろくんは ______________ に住んでいます。

2 山田たかひろくんは ______________ が大好きです。

3 山田たかひろくんは ______________ をすこしはなします。

4 おとうとさんのなまえは ______________ です。

5 山田たかひろくんはまつりで ______________ を食べました。

**24** Lots of まつり are held in Japan every year. Using the Internet, find information on some other まつり and fill in the grid below.
Here is a website to get you started: http://www.gergo.com/pauline/japan/festivals.htm

| まつりのなまえ | いつ？（—— 月 —— 日） | どこ？（町のなまえ） |
| --- | --- | --- |
| | | |
| | | |
| | | |
| | | |

## 25 かいてみよう

You have been invited to be a part of the team creating a website for the 日光(にっこう)のまつり. Your task is to write some introductory sentences in 日本語 for the headings below. Write these in the planning space provided. You could suggest appropriate images to accompany your text.

## 26

The tourist association in your town has heard about all the work you have been doing to promote 日光(にっこう) and its festival. They want to use your experience to write a blurb about your town and a local festival or parade so that it can promoted as a tourist event for Japanese tourists. You will of course need to include information such as where the town is (a map is handy), what the town is like, when the festival is, what it is like, if there is special food, and so on. You could attach some photos to add even more interest.

## 27 パズルあそび

There are eighteen places hidden horizontally and vertically in this puzzle. Find them and answer the questions below. Two particles will remain and you can use them to complete the sentence at the bottom of the page.

| | | | | | | | | | |
|---|---|---|---|---|---|---|---|---|---|
| と | え | き | レ | ス | ト | ラ | ン | へ | や |
| し | が | じ | ん | じ | ゃ | プ | ー | ル | え |
| ょ | っ | う | ス | ー | パ | ー | た | こ | い |
| か | こ | ち | に | わ | ま | ち | ん | う | が |
| ん | う | み | せ | や | ま | か | ぼ | え | か |
| き | ょ | う | し | つ | に | わ | が | ん | ん |

**1** Find five places that are written with these かんじ.

町 ________ 川 ________ 学校 ________

山 ________ 田んぼ ________

**2** Find five places that have only two ひらがな (and are not written above in かんじ).

________ ________ ________

________ ________

**3** Find three places that are written in カタカナ.

________ ________ ________

**4** Find five places that have more than two ひらがな (and are not written above in かんじ).

________ ________ ________

________ ________

ここ ____ やさしいパズル ____ あります。

# 第六課

## 1 かんじ

Practice writing these new かんじ.

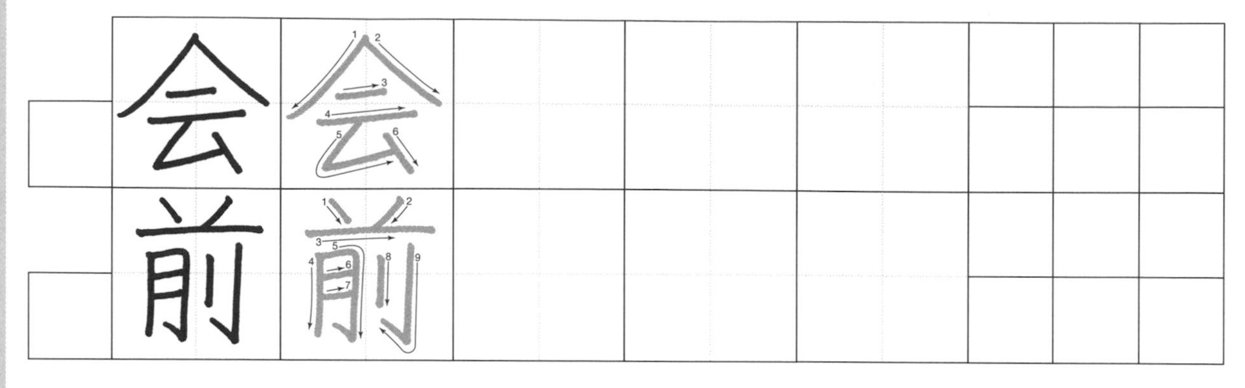


## 2 かんじ

Choose a verb from the box and write it under the appropriate picture.
きをつけて！– there is an extra verb.

| 行きます | 会います | 食べます | 生まれました | 見ます | 住んでいます |
|---|---|---|---|---|---|

## 3 かんじ

せん生's comment for ベンくん's last homework assignment was 'A very good piece. Shame you are not using the かんじ you know'.
ベンくん has asked you to help with his latest homework assignment which was an account of what he did on Saturday. He's written the words that should go in かんじ and wants you to write them in using ひらがな too, if needed.
Hope you both get a good grade!

せんしゅうの___ ___ ___ にデートに___ ___ ___ ___ ___ 。
どようび　いきました

___ で___ ___ ___ に___ ___ ___ ___ ___ 。ランチを___ ___ ___ ___ ___ 。
まち　ともだち　あいました　たべました

それから、えいがを___ ___ ___ ___ 。
みました

___ ___ ___ の名(な) ___ は___ ___ ___ ___ です。___ ___ ___ ___ は
ともだち　(な)まえ　ともこさん　ともこさん

___ ___ ___ です。大阪(おおさか)で___ ___ ___ ___ ___ ___ 。___ 、ここに
にほんじん　うまれました　いま

___ ___ ___ います。___ ___ ___ ___ は___ ___ がじょうずです。
すんで　ともこさん　えいご

ぼくは___ ___ ___ ___ が___ ___ ___ です。
ともこさん　だいすき

___ ___ ___ にうちにかえりました。
ろくじはん

## 4 かんじ

山川せん生 has put a list of times on the ドア of the 日本語のきょうしつ telling when she is free to give extra help. Jot these times down in your diary so that you have a record of them. The first has been done for you.

この時間(じかん)に日本語の手つだいができます！

月曜日の八時半
火曜日の一時二十分前
水曜日の四時十分前
木曜日の九時十五分前
金曜日の三時十五分

山川せん生

Japanese help!

Monday 8.30

## 5 かんじ

Here is some review on telling the time. Write these times in かんじ.

1 4.30
2 6.00
3 5.15
4 2.20
5 1/4 to 1.00
6 10 to 7.00
7 25 to 8.00
8 5 to 9.00

# パートA

**Arranging when and where to meet**

## 6 きいてみようA

あいさん is arranging to meet her friends and family – all over town! Listen as she arranges where to meet. Write the number of the conversation below the picture of the appropriate meeting place.

## 7 かいてみよう

Write these places in 日本語.

1 In front of the supermarket ______________________

2 In front of the school ______________________

3 In front of the picture theater ______________________

4 In front of the library ______________________

5 In front of Masako's house ______________________

## 8 きいてみようB

いま

These people are going to the movies and they have arranged to meet in front of the movie theater. Listen as they decide what time to meet and write down the time in the space provided.

1 ______________________

2 ______________________

3 ______________________

4 ______________________

5 ______________________

6 ______________________

7 ______________________

8 ______________________

## 9 かいてみよう

ようすけくん is arranging to go out with まさ子さん. Read his side of the conversation and answer these questions.

- Where is he going? ______________________
- Where will they meet? ______________________
- What time will they meet? ______________________

ローラーブレード？
こうえんで？
いいですね。

いいですね。
こうえんの前で会いましょう。
何時に会いましょうか。

3時ですか。いいですね。じゃ、
3時にこうえんの前で会いましょう。

## 10

Write what you would say in the following situations.

**1** You invite your friend to go shopping.

______________________________________________

**2** You ask where you should meet.

______________________________________________

**3** You suggest that you meet at 2.30.

______________________________________________

**4** You confirm that you'll meet at 2.30 in front of the department store.

______________________________________________

## 11 かいてみよう

All of these invitations for the weekend have been left on your answering machine by your Japanese friends. Someone has jotted them down for you and now you need to transfer where you are going and when and where you will meet into your diary. Write your answers in English.

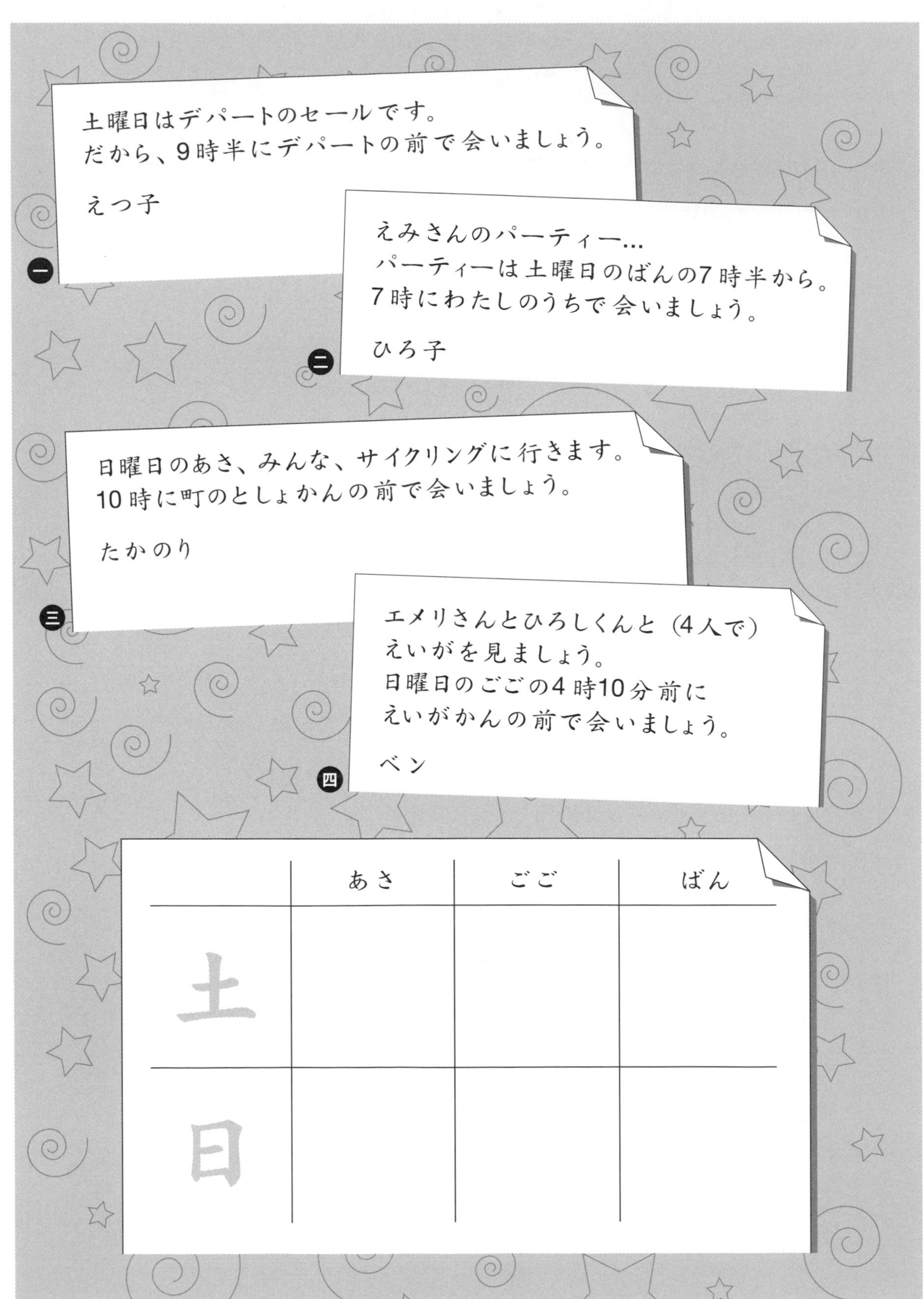

一

土曜日はデパートのセールです。
だから、9時半にデパートの前で会いましょう。

えつ子

二

えみさんのパーティー...
パーティーは土曜日のばんの7時半から。
7時にわたしのうちで会いましょう。

ひろ子

三

日曜日のあさ、みんな、サイクリングに行きます。
10時に町のとしょかんの前で会いましょう。

たかのり

四

エメリさんとひろしくんと（4人で）
えいがを見ましょう。
日曜日のごごの4時10分前に
えいがかんの前で会いましょう。

ベン

| | あさ | ごご | ばん |
|---|---|---|---|
| 土 | | | |
| 日 | | | |

## 12 かいてみよう

あきらくん is organizing for some friends to go out on Friday night. He has sent you the following email invitation. Send him back an email to accept and find out where to meet. You'll then need to ask about what time to meet. Don't forget to confirm the place and time.

送信者（そうしんしゃ）：山川晶 <akira_y@hotmail.com>

件名（けんめい）：レストランに

日付（ひづけ）：7月10日　21.45

Message from あきらくん：

金曜日のばん、いっしょに日本のレストランに行きませんか。

Reply to sender:

日付（ひづけ）：7月10日　21.50

Message from あきらくん：

日本のレストランの前で会いましょうか。

Reply to sender:

日付（ひづけ）：7月10日　22.00

Message from あきらくん：

6時半はどうですか。

Reply to sender:

## きいてみようC

なおこさん is often out when her friends call so they leave messages on her answering machine. Listen to this latest lot and write down the main information on the message paper.

一

メッセージ for Naoko

from Emi

The メッセージ is

............

............

............

............

二

メッセージ for Naoko

from Mark

The メッセージ is

............

............

............

............

三

メッセージ for Naoko

from Hiroshi

The メッセージ is

............

............

............

............

四

メッセージ for Naoko

from Atsuko

The メッセージ is

............

............

............

............

## 14 きいてみようD

Listen in on these conversations as people make arrangements for going places this weekend. Take notes for each conversation on the notepad. Listen for where they are going, when they are going and where and what at time they will meet.

一

going where?/doing what?

going when?

meeting where?

meeting when?

二

going where?/doing what?

going when?

meeting where?

meeting when?

三

going where?/doing what?

going when?

meeting where?

meeting when?

四

going where?/doing what?

going when?

meeting where?

meeting when?



いま

# パートB

**Floor levels, colors and clothes**

**15** かいてみよう

You are in 東京(とうきょう) buying some おみやげ for your family. Look at this デパート guide and work out to which floor you will go to buy or do the things on your list. The first one has been done for you.

1 Tシャツ（あに） 四かい

2 Tシャツ（いもうと） ________

3 ゴルフのシャツ（父） ________

4 日本のおかしとケーキ（母） ________

5 ランチを食べます ________

6 えいがを見ます ________

**店内ご案内**

| | |
|---|---|
| 6F | ワーナー・マイカル・シネマズ |
| 5F | レストランのフロア |
| 4F | メンズファッションと<br>アウトドア・スポーツのフロア |
| 3F | ヤングファッションのフロア |
| 2F | ハイファッションのフロア |
| 1F | 食料品のフロア |

**16** かいてみよう

Can you complete this 'highest building' statistic for your country?

日本で、一ばんたかいビルは70かいです。

____________________ で、一ばんたかいビルは ________ かいです。

**17** きいてみようE

まりえさん and ひろしくん are looking at a floor guide for a new store and planning where they would like to go. Listen to their conversation and write down what floor the following items are on.

## 18 かいてみよう

This is the first page of a まんが called ファッション・ボーイ.
ファッション・ボーイ is introducing himself and 'modelling' his first beach gear outfit with his sister. The writer of ファッション・ボーイ has supplied the following list of colors for the clothes pictured. Refer to his list and color in the beach scene.

| ファッション・ボーイ | いもうとさん | |
|---|---|---|
| きいろいぼうし | あおいぼうし | オレンジのバケツ |
| あかいポロシャツ | ピンクのTシャツ | カーキのタオル |
| みどりのショートパンツ | しろいスカート | |
| くろいスニーカー | こんのサンダル | |

What is ファッション・ボーイ wearing now? Name the items of clothing indicated by the numbers.

ファッション・ボーイのふく

1 ____________ 2 ____________ 3 ____________

4 ____________ 5 ____________ 6 ____________

7 ____________

## 19 きいてみようF

What are なおこさん and あいさん looking at, at the department store? Look at the pictures and then write the number of the conversation beside the appropriate picture.

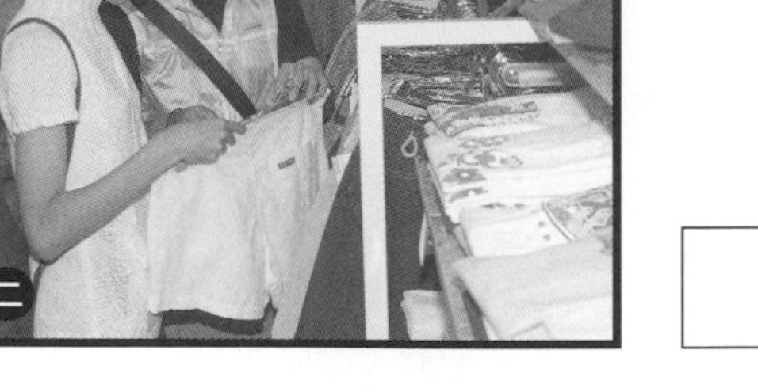

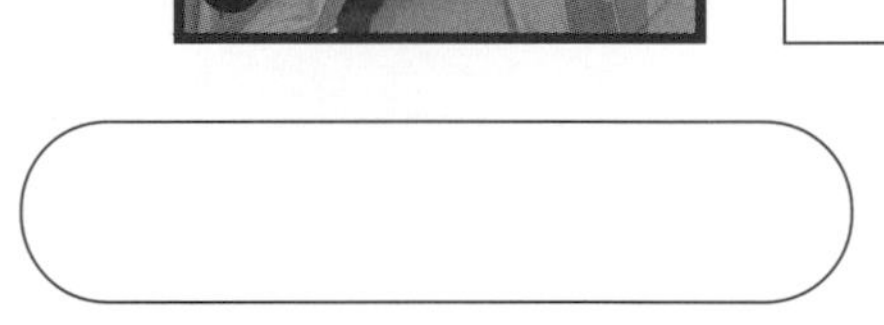

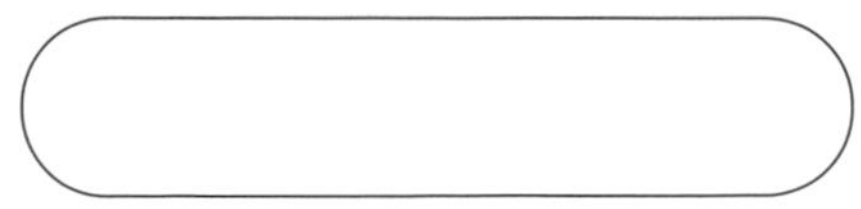

## 20 かいてみよう

Write labels for the items that なおこさん and あいさん are looking at.

## 21 よんでみよう

What is being advertised here?
How much do things cost?

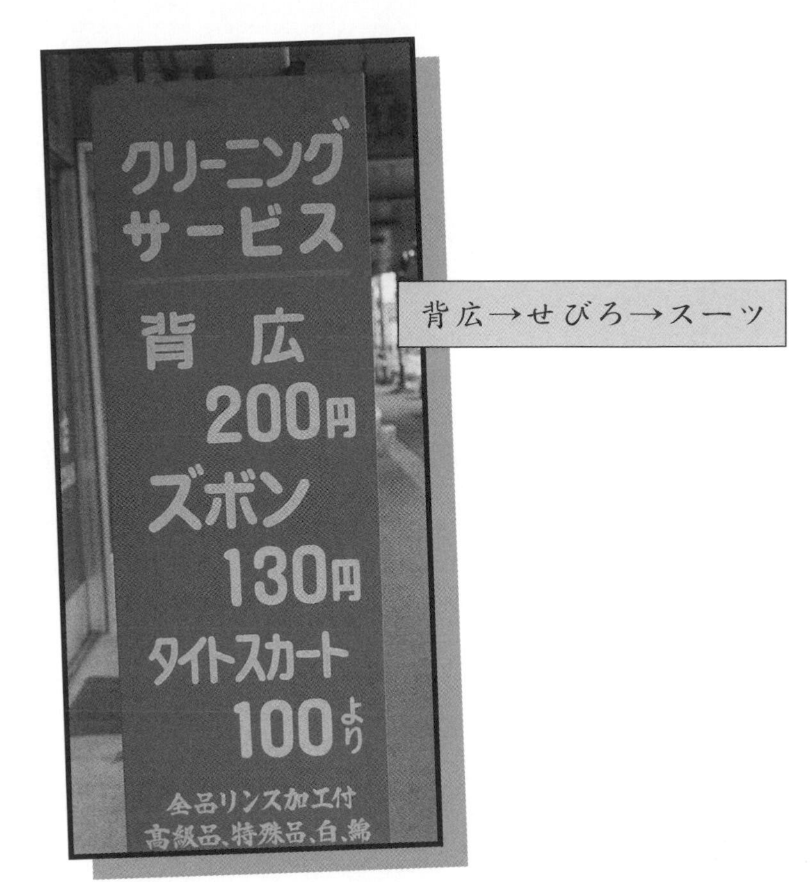


## 22 かいてみよう

You've arrived in 東京(とうきょう) to visit your pen pal for a few days. Unfortunately your luggage didn't catch the same plane as you and you won't have it for a couple of days. The airline has given you 15 000 円 to buy some new gear. Choose from the sale items on 128–9 ページ of your textbook and write a list of what you'll buy. If there is a choice, write in the color too. The weather is warm but it can get cold at night.

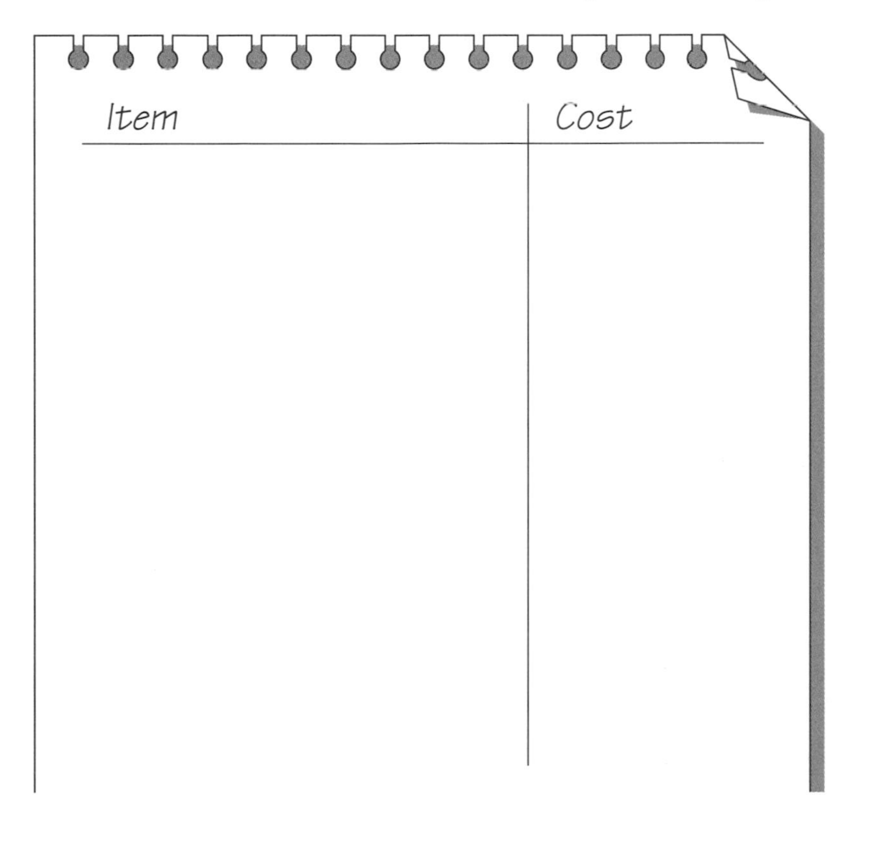

# パートC

It's not that weird!
What are you wearing?
Putting it together

## 23 かいてみよう

Complete these statements to give your opinion about who or what isn't weird, interesting, difficult and so on.

1 ______________ はそんなにへんじゃないです。
2 ______________ はおもしろくないです。
3 ______________ はすてきじゃないです。
4 ______________ はぜんぜんむずかしくないです。
5 ______________ はきれいじゃないです。
6 ______________ はつまらなくないです。
7 ______________ はハンサムじゃないです。
8 ______________ はよくないです。
9 ______________ はモダンじゃないです。
10 ______________ はおいしくないです。

## 24 かいてみよう

Disagree with the following statements. The first one has been done for you.

1 このくつはかわいいですね。いいえ、かわいくないです。
2 このぼうしはたかいですか。いいえ、______________
3 このジーンズはちょっとみじかいですね。いいえ、______________
4 くろいTシャツはやすいですね。いいえ、______________
5 このベストはいいですね。いいえ、______________
6 そのトレパンはあたらしいですか。いいえ、______________
7 このしろいスカートはすてきですね。いいえ、______________
8 このジャケットはへんですね。いいえ、______________
9 このピンクのポロシャツはきれいですね。いいえ、______________
10 このシャツのブランドはゆうめいですか。いいえ、______________

（ブランド brand name）

## ㉕ きいてみようG

りょうじくん doesn't like shopping and rejects the suggestions of his friends when they go out to buy new clothes. Why doesn't he buy the things they suggest?
Mark the appropriate circle.

一

○ doesn't like the color
○ doesn't like the price
○ some other reason

二

○ doesn't like the color
○ doesn't like the price
○ some other reason

三

○ doesn't like the color
○ doesn't like the price
○ some other reason

四

○ doesn't like the color
○ doesn't like the price
○ some other reason

五

○ doesn't like the color
○ doesn't like the price
○ some other reason

六

○ doesn't like the color
○ doesn't like the price
○ some other reason

**26** かいてみよう

Read the story ピンクのトレパン2 on 123 ページ of your textbook and write what あいさん and なおこさん thought about what they saw in OPA デパート.

| Item | What they thought |
|---|---|
| CDs | |
| blue hat | |
| black cap | |
| white shorts | |
| navy blue shorts | なおこさん: |
| | あいさん: |
| pink jumper | なおこさん: |
| | あいさん: |
| pink shoes | なおこさん: |
| | あいさん: |
| floral shoes | |
| checked jeans | |
| white vest | |
| pink track pants | なおこさん: |
| | あいさん: |

**27** かいてみよう

Back to you! 今、何をきていますか。せいふくをきていますか、しふく (clothes that are not a uniform) をきていますか。せつめいしてください。
Write a description of what you are wearing now.

**28** かいてみよう

しゅんごくん has a part-time job at 東京(とうきょう)ディズニーランド. Complete the statements below to describe his uniform.

くろいヘルメットを ______________________________

しろいシャツを ______________________________

しろいズボンを ______________________________

くろいローラーブレードを ______________________________

**29** You sometimes read in magazines lists of best-dressed and worst-dressed famous people. Who do you think might qualify for one of these categories? Think of someone, get a picture and write a nomination for them. Your nomination should include:

- The person's name and why they are famous. Are they a pop-star, sports personality, TV or movie star...
- A description of the person. Are they tall, short, dark-haired, long-haired...
- A description of what they are wearing, including the color of the clothes...
- Your opinion of what they are wearing. Does the outfit suit them, is it cool, not that interesting, really strange, fabulously expensive, cheap chic...

## 30 きいてみようH

Try to identify the people below by what they are wearing. Listen as a description is read to you and draw a line to match the name and photo.

一 はる子さん

二 ゆうたくん

三 あつしくん

四 なおみさん

五 だいすけくん

六 友子さん

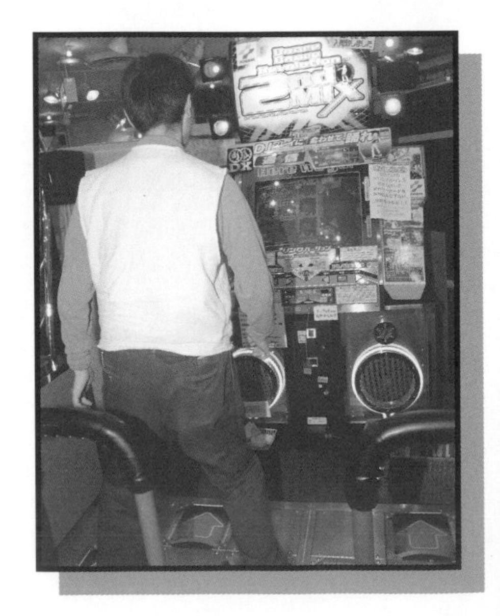

## 31 パズルあそび

あいさん is helping なお子さん to decide which clothes she should wear out today. Below is a list of the clothes they are looking at and the comments あいさん is making. Put these into 日本語 in the puzzle and the shaded letters will spell out what なお子さん is wearing.

1 green dress

2 orange hat

3 blue slacks

4 brown shoes

5 yellow vest

6 red windbreaker

7 navy blue shorts

8 black jeans

9 を

10 gray jumper

11 It's not pretty. 。

12 They're not nice. 。

13 It's not cute. 。

14 It's not boring. 。

15 They're not cheap. 。

なお子さんは ________________________ 。

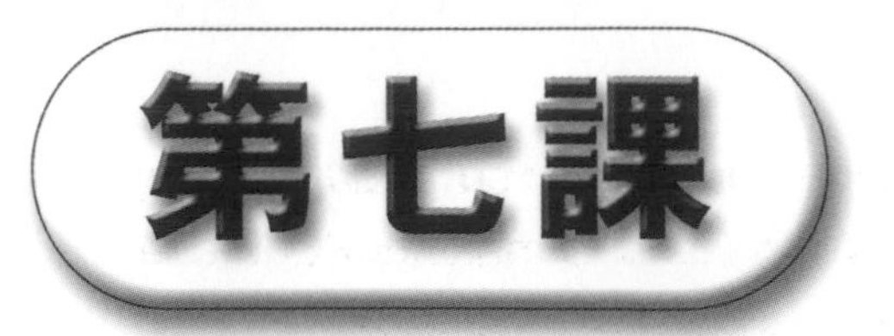

# 第七課

## 1 かんじ

Practice writing these new かんじ.

| | | | | | | | |
|---|---|---|---|---|---|---|---|
| 雨 | 雨 | | | | | | |
| 天 | 天 | | | | | | |
| 気 | 気 | | | | | | |

## しってる？

- You have seen 日, meaning *day* or *sun*, used in lots of words and with different readings. Show that you know many of the readings for this かんじ by writing ふりがな above these words.

日本　　日曜日　　三日　　十三日　　父の日

Remember 父(ちち) の 日(ひ)? For special or particular days, 日 is read ひ. Read aloud these days and then work out what they are.

**1** 母の日 ______________________

**2** その日 ______________________

**3** 雨の日 ______________________

**4** つぎの日 ______________________

**5** トーナメントの日 ______________________

## かんじ

Draw lines connecting each of these かんじ with its reading and its English meaning.

| | | | |
|---|---|---|---|
| 1 | 雨 | まち | English |
| 2 | 英語 | にんき | rain |
| 3 | 町 | てんき | popularity |
| 4 | 天気 | まえ | like |
| 5 | 前 | あめ | in front of |
| 6 | 好き | えいご | weather |
| 7 | 人気 | すき | town |

英 英 英

## かんじ

People are commenting on the awful rain and also on the good weather. Write what they are saying, using かんじ and ひらがな, in the speech bubbles.

# パートA

What's the weather like?

**4** かいてみよう

Read the weather forecasts for four cities in Japan and, using the weather symbols given below, prepare the map for the 7時のニュース. Don't forget to write in the temperature too.

札幌（さっぽろ）はゆきでしょう。きおんはマイナス5どでしょう。
東京（とうきょう）ははれのち雨でしょう。きおんは10どでしょう。
広島（ひろしま）ははれ時々くもりでしょう。きおんは13どでしょう。
鹿児島（かごしま）はくもりのち雨でしょう。きおんは14どでしょう。

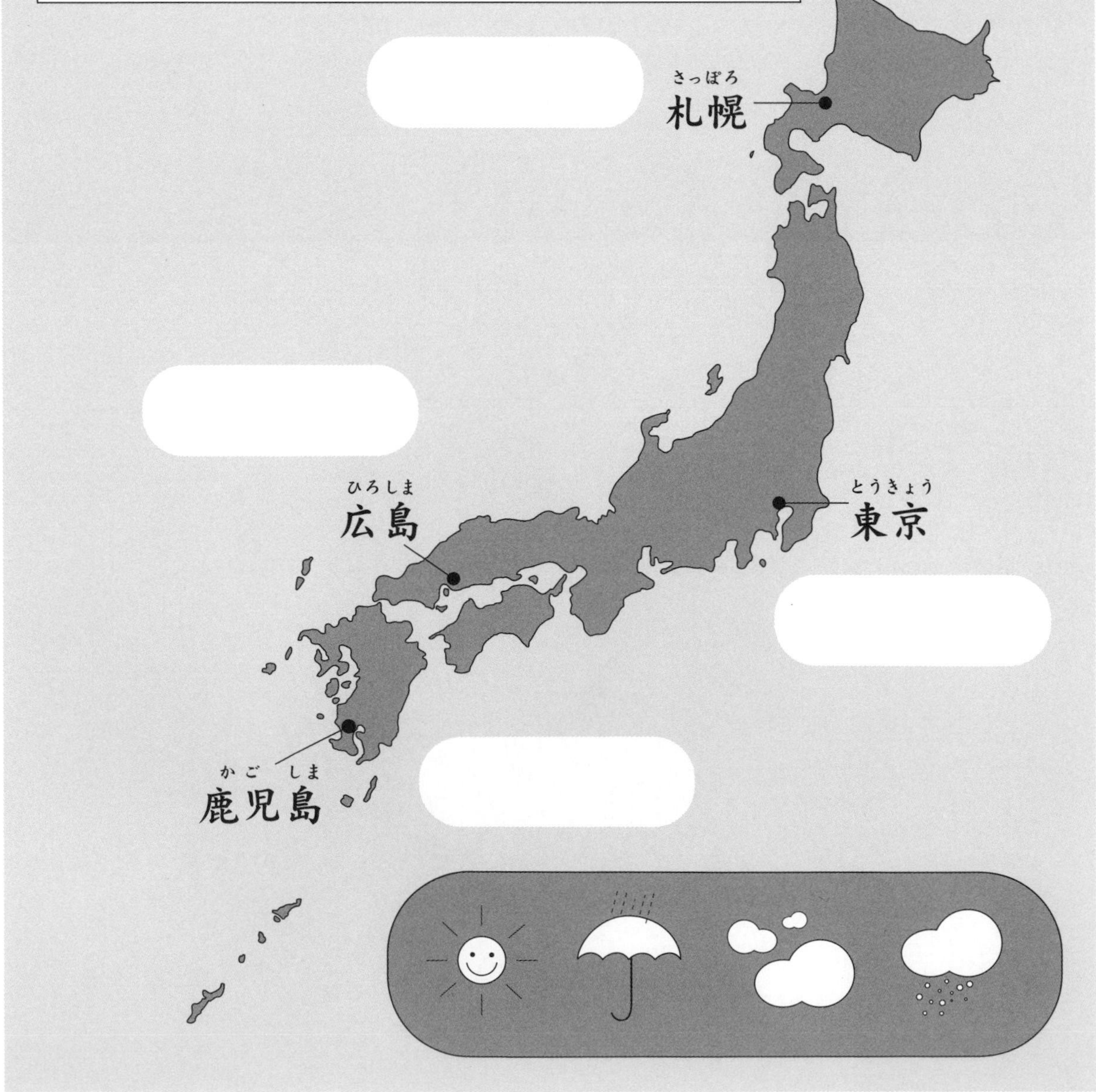

札幌（さっぽろ）
東京（とうきょう）
広島（ひろしま）
鹿児島（かごしま）

## 5 きいてみようA

Listen to the weather forecast for cities around Japan. Highlight the appropriate symbols and write down the expected temperature.

What is the weather like where you are? Write the forecast for today.

______________________________

______________________________

______________________________

## 6 かいてみよう

きこうさん, the weather forecaster, got caught up in some bad weather coming to the studio and has asked you to prepare his script for tomorrow's weather for the following cities. Here is the information to write into the script below.

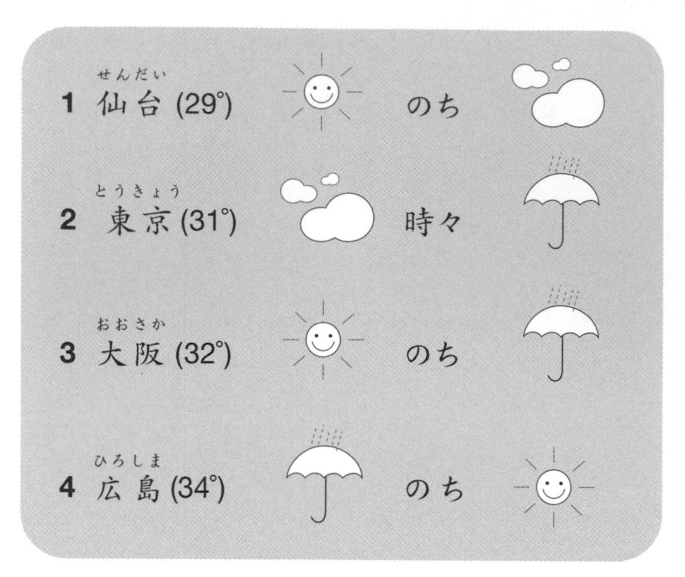

5月25日の天気よほうです。

あしたの天気です。

あした、せんだいは ______________________________ 。

きおんは ______________________________ 。

あした、とうきょうは ______________________________ 。

きおんは ______________________________ 。

あした、おおさかは ______________________________ 。

きおんは ______________________________ 。

あした、ひろしまは ______________________________ 。

きおんは ______________________________ 。

## 7 きいてみようB

めぐみさん and さとしくん are going on a world trip! Listen as they read the weather forecasts for cities around the world to help them decide where to go. Highlight the appropriate symbol and write down the temperature.

1 ホノルル
Honolulu

_____ ℃

2 サンフランシスコ
San Francisco

_____ ℃

3 トロント
Toronto

_____ ℃

4 ニューヨーク
New York

_____ ℃

5 ロンドン
London

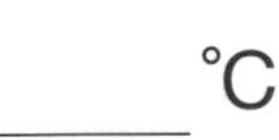
_____ ℃

6 ヘルシンキ
Helsinki

_____ ℃

7 カイロ
Cairo

_____ ℃

8 シンガポール
Singapore

_____ ℃

9 シドニー
Sydney

_____ ℃

10 オークランド
Auckland

_____ ℃

# パートB

What are you doing?

## 8 かいてみよう

Complete these tables with the て or ～ます form of each verb.

**Group 1**

| ～ます | て |
|---|---|
| かいます | |
| 会います | |
| うたいます | |
| | きいて |
| かきます | |
| | はいて |
| | あるいて |
| 行きます | |
| およぎます | |
| はなします | |
| | かして |
| | まって |
| たちます (stand) | |
| しにます | |
| あそびます | |
| のみます | |
| よみます | |
| | 住んで |
| かえります | |
| とります | |
| つくります | |
| あります | |
| | がんばって |
| | すわって |
| | かぶって |
| | |

**Group 2**

| ～ます | て |
|---|---|
| 食べます | |
| ねます | |
| かけます | |
| 生まれます | |
| | 見せて |
| 見ます | |
| おきます | |
| できます | |
| います | |

**Irregular**

| ～ます | て |
|---|---|
| します | |

## 9 かいてみよう

What are these people doing? For each picture, write a caption to explain what the person is doing. There are some 'doing verbs' in the box below that you can use.

| | | |
|---|---|---|
| のんでいます | まっています | よんでいます |
| うたっています | とっています | かっています |
| はなしています | かいています | きいています |

## 10 きいてみようC

What are these people doing? Listen to these conversations about the people in the photos and write the number of the dialogue under the appropriate photo.

一 

二 

三 

四 

五 

六 

## 11 かいてみよう

Here are some verbs that you haven't yet learned. However, you can use the patterns for the て form to work out the て form of these verbs too. がんばって！

| 〜ます | て |
|---|---|
| あらいます (wash) | |
| ひらきます (open) | |
| だします (put out) | |
| もちます (hold) | |
| とびます (fly) | |
| かみます (chew) | |
| のります (ride on) | |
| 見つけます (find) | |

本をひらいています。

ガムをかんでいます。

## 12 かいてみよう

Choose a time of the day and freeze it – what is everyone at home or school doing at this time? ジョーくん has chosen 金曜日のばんの六時. Read his account of what the people in his family are doing and use it as a model to write an account about your family or friends.

金曜日のばんの六時

母はテレビを見ています。おかしを食べています。

父はスーパーでかいものをしています。ばんごはんをかっています。

あねはでんわをかけています。

おとうとはコンピューターゲームをしています。

ぼくは日本語のしゅくだいをしています。（うそ！）

## ⑬ きいてみようD

Who is doing what in 田口先生's class? Listen to this conversation about what the people in the class are doing and write the number of the person in the box next to them on the illustration.

| | | | | |
|---|---|---|---|---|
| 1 ふみえさん | 2 えみさん | 3 あつ子さん | 4 たかのりくん | 5 みち子さん |
| 6 しゅんごくん | 7 みどりさん | 8 じゅんいちくん | 9 田口先生 | 10 ただしくん |

# パートC Putting it together

**14** かいてみよう

Look at the pictures and read the photo story イッツエキサイティング！ which starts on 141ページ of your textbook. Then answer the questions below.

1 今日はどんな天気ですか。きおんは何どですか。

2 さちえさんはどこにいますか。だれといますか。

3 さちえさんは何をきていますか。

4 やえさんは何をきていますか。

5 四人の女の子はどこに行きますか。どうやって行きますか。

6 バスケットボールぶの男の子は何をしていますか。

7 カラオケスタジオはいくらですか。たかいですか。

8 女の子はカラオケスタジオで何をしていますか。
（四つかいてください – write 4 things）

## 15 パズルあそび

In the photo story, イッツエキサイティング！, how did people say the following things? Write the answer in the squares using ひらがな, カタカナ, and かんじ and the circled letters will spell out a useful question.

1 Why don't we go to karaoke?

2 The temperature is 23 degrees.

23

3 Sayuri, wait.

4 The weather is cloudy.

5 It's not that expensive, is it?

6 Next is Yae.

7 They got thirsty.

8 Now they are having a coke.

9 See you tomorrow.

10 Goodbye.

11 Today was fun, wasn't it?

よ

## 16 よんでみよう

Look at the picture and read Taka's phone conversation on 151ページ of your textbook. Then read each statement below and circle ○（まる）if it is correct and ✕（ばつ）if it is incorrect.

1 たかくんは、今、うちにいます。 ○ ✕
2 今日、日光(にっこう)は雨です。 ○ ✕
3 たかくんは日光(にっこう)でまつりを見ました。 ○ ✕
4 たかくんのおじいさんはねています。 ○ ✕
5 お父さんはたかくんとはなしています。 ○ ✕
6 おとうとさんはおんがくをきいています。 ○ ✕
7 いもうとさんはチョコレートを食べています。 ○ ✕
8 ねこもチョコレートを食べています。 ○ ✕
9 いぬは水をのんでいます。 ○ ✕
10 お母さんはテレビを見ています。 ○ ✕

## 17 きいてみようE

Two Japanese students who are overseas for the first time are calling home to talk to their moms. Listen to what they talk about and fill in the details below.

*calling from?:*

*time overseas:*

*weather overseas:*

*news at home:*

*calling from?:*

*time overseas:*

*weather overseas:*

*news at home:*

18 かいてみよう

おめでとう！You have been chosen by a radio station to conduct a phone interview with ひさし from グレイ prior to his tour of your country. You can ask 8–10 questions, but the management of ひさし want to see your list of questions before the interview.
You can find out where he was born, where he lives now, where he is at this moment, what he is doing, what he is wearing, what the weather is like, what kind of girlfriend he has... Put the following headings on your question list.

## グレイのひさしのインタビュー

スクリプト

第七課

## 19 きいてみようF

Play 'Eliminator' by listening to three hints about each of the pictures below. As you listen to each statement, you will find that it does not apply to one person – you can eliminate them! You will finally be left with one person that best fits the description given in the statements.

## 20 パズルあそび

Complete this クロスワードパズル. Write all your answers in ひらがな and カタカナ.

**たて↓**

**1** It means 'empty orchestra'.

**2** You can sing various kinds of these.

**4** I bought *nine* hamburgers!

**5** That really *suits* you.

**6** Look, *there's* a parade.

**9** *What kind of* weather?

**10** It's really *hot* today.

**13** The *temperature* will be 32°.

**15** He's *writing* a book! 本を ____________ います。

**17** やすくないです。____________ です。

**18** I'm listening! ____________ います。

**19** Let's meet in front of the station. ____________で会いましょう。

**20** Where will we meet? ____________ 会いましょうか。

**21** 'Hello' on the phone.

## よこ→

**3** A popular drink – particularly while singing!

**4** Do you know the test *answer*?

**7** The weather will be *rainy and cloudy later*.

**8** I'm thirsty! ____________ がかわきました。

**10** He bought some *red* sandals.

**11** It's 町 in かんじ, ____________ in ひらがな.

**12** *Nice* shoes!

**14** It's on the *7th floor*.

**16** I've got a headache. あたまが____________ です。

**18** He's *wearing* a cool T-shirt. かっこいいTシャツを____________ います。

**22** It's very *crowded*.

**23** He's drinking a glass of milk. ミルクを ____________ います。

**24** See you tomorrow.

**25** Let's meet in front of the movie theater.

____________ の前で会いましょう。

# 第八課

## 1 かんじ

Practice writing this new かんじ.

小 小

## 2 かんじ

Draw lines to match two words that are related. One has been done for you.

月曜日
食べます
小さい
川
日本語
父 —— 母
大きい
耳
学生
男
会います
水
雨
英語
目
学校
金曜日
山
女

**3** かんじ

The 小学生 pictured on 167ページ of your textbook has sent the following letter to your little brother and he wants to know what it says. Give him a summary of her letter under the headings below.

James くんへ、
今日は。わたしの名(な)前は山口さえ子です。10さいです。小学6年生です。
学校で英語をべんきょうしています。でも、まだへたです。

東京(とうきょう)で生まれました。今、前田に住んでいます。前田は小さい町です。
うちも小さいです。うちのそばに川と田んぼがあります。とてもしずかです。

かぞくは4人です。父と母とあにです。父はジャーナリストです。
母は小学校の先(せん)生です。

わたしは、ひまな時、スポーツをします。バスケットボールとバレボール
をします。時々、かぞくと山にハイキングに行きます。

James くん、はやく、てがみをかいてね。まっています。
さえ子より

Name ______________________ Age ________

School details

______________________________

Where she lives

town

______________________________

house

______________________________

______________________________

Family

______________________________

______________________________

What she likes doing

______________________________

______________________________

## 4 かんじ

This クロスワード has been done in ひらがな. Write かんじ clues for it.

| 1 ち | い | さ | い | | | | 2 お | | | 3 と | | 4 ひ | |
|---|---|---|---|---|---|---|---|---|---|---|---|---|---|
| ち | | | | | | | お | | | も | | ゃ | |
| | | | 5 ま | | 6 な | | き | | | こ | | 7 く | ち |
| | | 8 い | ち | ね | ん | せ | い | | | さ | | え | |
| 9 て | ん | き | | | に | | | 10 に | ほ | ん | じ | ん | |
| | | ま | | 11 は | ち | じ | は | ん | | | | | |
| | | 12 す | き | | | | | 13 き | ん | よ | う | び | |

### ヒント

**よこ→**

1 ________ 7 ________

8 ________ 9 ________

10 ________ 11 ________

12 ________ 13 ________

**たて↓**

1 ________ 2 ________

3 ________ 4 ________

5 ________ 6 ________

8 ________ 10 ________

Make a request
Give an instruction

## 5 きいてみようA

What would you do if you were to obediently follow these instructions?

| | | | |
|---|---|---|---|
| 1 | go to the front | write your name | listen for your name |
| 2 | do something quietly | do something quickly | do your homework |
| 3 | write | wait | listen |
| 4 | look at the video | turn around | show a video |
| 5 | bring a tape | play a tape | listen to a tape |
| 6 | read aloud | read quietly | have a drink |
| 7 | study a lot | practice a lot | do your homework |
| 8 | study Japanese | read your Japanese text | speak Japanese |

## 6 かいてみよう

A Japanese family nearby have asked you to babysit their three children for the evening. Last time you did this it was a bit chaotic, so this time you've decided to write out some appropriate instructions and requests in 日本語 and go prepared!

1 Do your piano practice.

_______________

2 Watch the TV quietly.（しずかに）

_______________

3 Eat your banana.

_______________

4 Drink your milk.

_______________

5 Wait!

_______________

6 Sing us a song.

_______________

7 Listen to the music.

_______________

8 Put on your pyjamas.（パジャマ）

_______________

9 Go to your room.

_______________

10 Go to sleep.

_______________

## 7 きいてみようB

These people (dogs are people too!) have been asked to do something. Write the number of the conversation in the box under the appropriate picture.

一

二

三

四

五

六

七

八

## 8 かいてみよう

You've been employed by 'ads r us' to write some short ads in 日本語. A fellow employee has written this one for a ride at 後楽園(こうらくえん)ゆうえんち. Write ads for the following things: some summer sandals, a new sushi restaurant, and the parade at Disneyland.

これはスカイフラワーです。
すごいですね！
チケットはたかくないです！
どうぞ。のってください。

# パートB

I did this, then this, then this...

## 9 かいてみよう

These sequences of pictures show what ケーティさん, レーチェルさん and ダーグくん did yesterday after they came home from school. Describe what each person did in the space given.

## 10 かいてみよう

What did you do after you got home from school yesterday? Write at least 3–4 things.

## 11 きいてみようC

These people were all asked about what they did yesterday. Jane was trying to write it all down but kept getting distracted – you can see the result below! Finish her work by listening to what the people did and completing her summary in English.

一

のり子さん

went to Tokyo Dome

________________

ate popcorn

at 6.00, ________________

________________

二

こうじくん

________________

went to Disneyland

________________

________________

hung around.

三

あきひろくん

________________

________________

bought a new T-shirt.

四

がくくん

went to the park

________________

________________

________________

saw a film.

五

ふみえさん

met her boyfriend

________________

had a hamburger

________________

________________

六

なお子さん

________________

went to the department store

________________

had a ________________

________________

七

さちえさん

met friends after school

________________

________________

at 5.00, ________________

did her homework.

八

田口さん

________________

at 8.00, ________

had udon noodles

________________

at 12.00, went to bed

## 12 よんでみよう

For English homework がくくん wrote a description of what he did on Sunday. Unfortunately the computer broke down and がくくん didn't get time to put what he did in order. Help him out by reading notes in his diary below and use it to write numbers next to the description showing the order in which he did things.

Had breakfast ________

Had a shake at McDonald's after the movie ________

Had a talk with the basketball club guys ________

Rang Fumie at 1.30 and had a talk ________

No loud mates at McDonald's this time! ________

Went to town with Hiroshi ________

Met Hiroshi at the station at 10.00 ________

Met the girls outside the picture theater ________

Got up at 9.00 ________

Went to school ________

Saw a movie ________

Had basketball practice till 1.00 ________

Had a great time ________

日曜日　はれ

9時におきて、あさごはんを食べて、10時にえきでひろしくんに会って、
学校に行きました。学校でバスケットボールぶの友だちとはなして、
1時までバスケットボールのれんしゅうをしました。

1時半にふみえさんにでんわをかけて、すこしはなしました。
それから、ひろしくんと町に行って、えいがかんの前で
ふみえさんときみこさんに会いました。4人でえいがを見ました。

えいがのあと、マクドナルドでシェーキをのみました。
ぼくのうるさい友だちはいませんでした。だから、とてもたのしかったです。

**13** かいてみよう

Since がくくん had to write about his day in 英語, he thinks that it is only fair that you write about yours in 日本語. Write notes in your diary explaining about a day that you have enjoyed recently. Try to give lots of information. You can use がくくん's diary as a model. You don't have to get too tied down with accurate details...!

# パートC

It's in front of the station and behind the Big Egg...

**14** かいてみよう

この人はどこにいますか。

Look at the picture and see how many answers you can write to this question. These words may help: きょうしつ, まど (window).

せん生

あいさん

## 15 かいてみよう

Look at the map of the area around the 東京ドーム and complete these statements using 前, そば and うしろ. You are at Gate 22. (The main entrance of 東京ドーム, 後楽園ゆうえんち and プリズムホール is each marked with an X.)

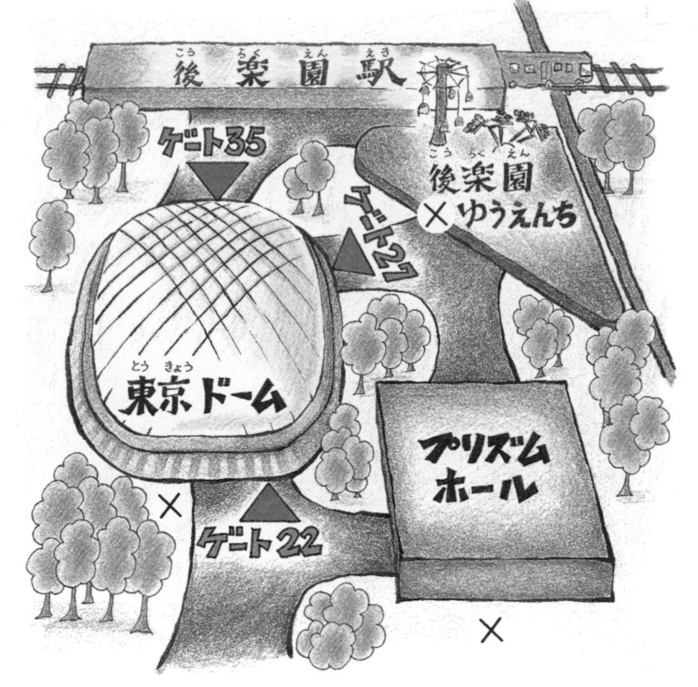


1 東京ドームは後楽園ゆうえんちの__________にあります。

2 東京ドームは後楽園えきの__________にあります。

3 プリズムホールは後楽園ゆうえんちの__________にあります。

4 プリズムホールは東京ドームの__________にあります。

5 後楽園ゆうえんちは東京ドームの__________にあります。

6 後楽園ゆうえんちはプリズムホールの__________にあります。

7 後楽園ゆうえんちは後楽園えきの__________にあります。

8 ゲート35は後楽園えきの__________にあります。

9 ゲート27は後楽園ゆうえんちの__________にあります。

10 ゲート22は東京ドームの__________にあります。

## 16 よんでみよう

Some people are waiting for friends at various places on the map on the opposite page. They are describing where they are on their mobile phones. Read the descriptions and write the number of the person in the appropriate location.

1 ゆりさん　わたしは後楽園(こうらくえん)ゆうえんちの前にいます。はやくね！

2 ひろくん　ぼくはプリズムホールのうしろにいます。まっていますよ。

3 えみさん　わたしは東京(とうきょう)ドームの前にいます。ゲート22のそばにいます。

4 たかくん　ぼくはゲート35の前にいます。東京(とうきょう)ドームのうしろにいますよ。

5 だいくん　ぼくは東京(とうきょう)ドームにいます。やきゅうを見ています。

6 まりさん　わたしは後楽園(こうらくえん)ゆうえんちにいます。ツインハリケーンにのっています。

## 17 かいてみよう

Look around you. Where are you? Who or what is in front of, near and behind you? Write 3–5 sentences.

______________________________

______________________________

______________________________

______________________________

______________________________

______________________________

## 18 きいてみようD

かよ子さん is showing Nick a photo of a picnic she had with her friends recently. Nick hasn't met all of かよ子さん's friends yet so he asks her about the people in the photo. Listen to their conversation and draw a line from each name to the appropriate person in the picture. 二 has been done for you.

一 だいじろうくん　　二 えつ子さん　　三 さわ子さん

四 けんたろうくん　　五 かつゆきくん　　六 かよ子さん

# パートD　Putting it together



## 19 きいてみようE

Use a highlighter to track the sequence of this conversation.

あきくん、/ えりさん、　東京（とうきょう）ディズニーランドに行きませんか。

東京（とうきょう）ディズニーランド？　いいですね。行きましょう。

じゃあ、行きましょう。

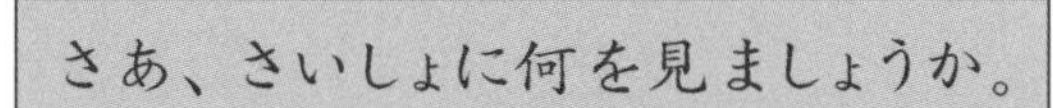

さあ、さいしょに何を見ましょうか。

そうですね。　パレード / ショー　を見ましょう。

ねえ、　あきくん、/ えりさん、　あの女の子は何をしていますか。

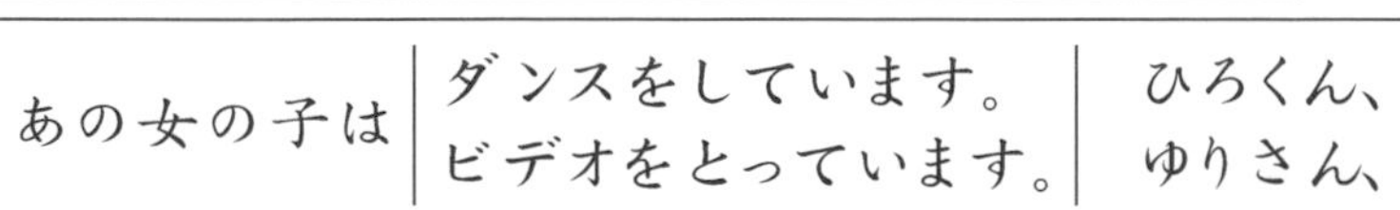

あの女の子は　ダンスをしています。/ ビデオをとっています。　ひろくん、/ ゆりさん、　のりものはどうですか。

いいですね。　ビッグサンダー マウンテン / スプラッシュマウンテン　にのりましょう。

ビッグサンダーマウンテン / スプラッシュマウンテン　は　すごかった / よかった / たのしかった　ですね。

ええ。こんどは、ゆうめいな　フック / スクルージ　としゃしんをとりましょう。

いいですね。　ひろくん、/ ゆりさん、　フック / スクルージ　といっしょにたってください。

ディズニーランドは　エキサイティング / きれい　でしたね。

そうですね。また行きましょう。

**20** かいてみよう

You took these photos when you visited 東京（とうきょう）ディズニーランド last year.
Before you put them in your photo album, write some interesting captions for them.

## 21 よんでみよう

Read the photo story 東京(とうきょう)ドームに行って... which starts on 156ページ of your textbook, then highlight whether the following statements are TRUE or FALSE.

1 You can have thrills and exciting adventures at Korakuen Amusement Park. Ⓣ Ⓕ

2 People are lining up to buy tickets for Korakuen Amusement Park. Ⓣ Ⓕ

3 The baseball team from Osaka is called the Kintetsu Buffaloes. Ⓣ Ⓕ

4 The scoreboard says that Rose and Clark play baseball for the Buffaloes. Ⓣ Ⓕ

5 The Buffaloes' cheer leader wears a red baseball uniform. Ⓣ Ⓕ

6 The fans protest really loudly when Clark goes out. Ⓣ Ⓕ

7 The cheer leaders of both teams have trumpet bands. Ⓣ Ⓕ

8 Food and drinks are banned at Tokyo Dome. Ⓣ Ⓕ

## 22 かいてみよう

Fill in the spaces with the correct particles to describe some scenes at the baseball. Use に, で or を.

1 東京(とうきょう)ドームは後楽園(こうらくえん)ゆうえんちのそば_____ あります。

2 ファンは東京(とうきょう)ドーム_____ やきゅうのしあい_____ 見ます。

3 おうえんだんの人ははっぴ_____ きています。

そして、ファンの前_____ おうえんをしています。

4 ファンはコカコーラ_____ のんでいます。

5 東京(とうきょう)ドーム_____ おべんとう_____ 食べています。

## ㉓ よんでみよう

These people were seen at the baseball. Write the number of each person next to the appropriate description.

バファローズの大ファンです。
友だちのてつやくんとやきゅうのしあいを見ます。
大阪（おおさか）に住んでいます。 ☐

ファイターズのファンです。
一人でやきゅうのしあいを見ます。
めがねをかけています。 ☐

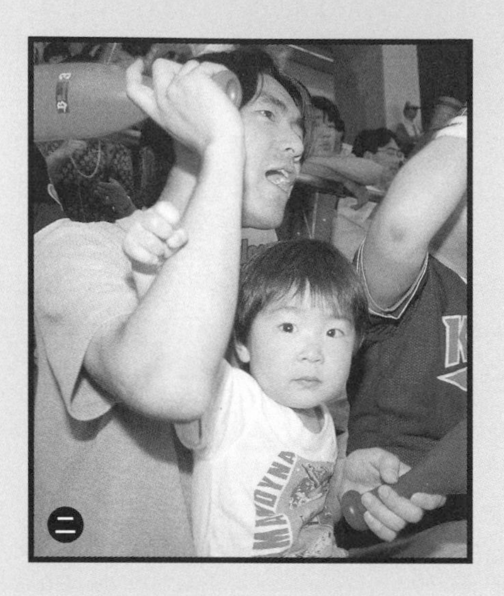

ビッグエッグでしごとをしています。
ユニフォームをきています。
わたしはポップコーンガールです。 ☐

バファローズのファンです。
お父さんといっしょに
やきゅうのしあいを見ます。
ぼくは小さい子どもです。 ☐

**24** よんでみよう

Read おもしろい日本 on 170–1ページ of your textbook. Select the correct answer from the alternatives given and write the Japanese sentence from the story which supports your answer.

**1** Noriko is presently:
- a) looking for something to do
- b) watching the baseball
- c) at the Tokyo Dome's baseball shop

________________________________________________

**2** Noriko's favorite player is:
- a) Daisuke Matsuzaka
- b) Seibu Lions
- c) Clark

________________________________________________

**3** Noriko buys a:
- a) phone card
- b) number 18 T-shirt
- c) poster

________________________________________________

**4** Noriko agrees with the phrase:
- a) No hit, no run
- b) Dai-chan, dai-suki
- c) Rookie sensation

________________________________________________

**25** よんでみよう

A profile of Daisuke Matsuzaka has been written for a magazine but the information is incomplete. Read his profile on 171ページ of your textbook and fill in the spaces.

Daisuke Matsuzaka was born in ____________ on ____________ . He went to school in ____________ . As soon as he finished school in ____________ 1999, he became a ____________ for the ____________ ____________. At 18, he became a ____________ ____________ . His ____________ is 155 kph. His personal slogan is ______________________ . For those non-sporting readers, this means ______________________________ .

# 今2のうた

日本

日本語

日本語今二

今、今、今

## カタカナ

おなかがすきましたか。
はい、はい。おなかすいた！
チキンラップ、ハンバーガー
ハムラップ、サラダ
のどがかわきましたか。
はい、はい。のみましょう！

＊ カタカナ、ひらがな、かんじも
日本語今、行きましょう！
かぞくと、せんせいと、ともだちも
日本語今、行きましょう！

これはいくらですか。
さんぜんろっぴゃく円。
さんぜんろっぴゃく円？
ああ、そうですか。
ありがとう！サンキュー！
さあ、カタカナに行きますよ！
(さあ、今！)

＊(くりかえし)

## 第一課

日本でうまれましたか。
はい、はい。日本人です。
オーストラリア、アメリカ
ニュージーランド、かんこく
日本語をはなしますか。
はい、はい。はなしましょう！

＊(くりかえし)

めがねをかけていますか。
いいえ、かけていません。
かみがきんぱつですか。
かみがちゃいろです。
ありがとう！サンキュー！
さあ、第一課に行きますよ！
(さあ、今！)

＊(くりかえし)

## 第二課

今、きょうしつにいますか。
はい、はい。いますよ。
あし、ゆび、かお、て
みみ、はな、くち、め
はる子さん、どうしたんですか。
手くびが、いたい！いたい！

＊(くりかえし)

くすりをのんでください。
はい、はい。かわいそうに！
ダブルフォルト！ざんねんだ！
サーブはすごい、すごい！
ありがとう！サンキュー！
さあ、第二課に行きますよ。
(さあ、今！)

＊(くりかえし)

## 第三課

町に行きませんか。
はい、はい。いいですね。
もしもし。ぼくですが…
もしもし。今日は。
あしたはどうですか。
はい、はい。行きましょう！

＊(くりかえし)

テニスはどうですか。
テニスはちょっと…
えいがに行きませんか。
はい、はい。いいですね。
ありがとう！サンキュー！
さあ、第三課に行きますよ！
(さあ、今！)

＊(くりかえし)

## 第四課

カレーライス、おねがいします。
はい、はい。カレーライス。
一つ、二つ、三つ、四つ
カフェラテ、アイスコーヒー
いらっしゃいませ。ごちゅうもんは？
ええと。おいしそう！

＊(くりかえし)

おのみものは？
いいえ、けっこうです。
フライドポテト三つですか。
はやく、たべましょう！
ありがとう、サンキュー！
さあ、第四課にいきますよ！
（さあ、今！）

＊（くりかえし）

## 第五課

日光に行きましょう！
はい、はい。行きましょう。
やきそば、たこやき
クレープ、バナナチョコ
まつりはこんでいますね。
はい、はい。こんでいます。

＊（くりかえし）

うちの前、何がありますが。
スーパー、こうえん、レストラン
田んぼ、山、テニスコート
ああ、すごいですね。
ありがとう！サンキュー！
さあ、第五課に行きますよ！
（さあ、今！）

＊（くりかえし）

## 第六課

会いましょうか。
はい、はい。えきの前…
くつ、セーター、Tシャツ
しろい、くろい、ピンク
ぼうしをかぶっていますか。
はい、はい。かぶっています。

＊（くりかえし）

ファッションフロアは何かいですか。
ろっかいとはっかいです。
ろっかいとはっかいですか。
ああ、そうですか。
ありがとう！サンキュー！
さあ、第六課に行きますよ！
（さあ、今！）

＊（くりかえし）

## 第七課

あしたははれでしょう。
はい、はい。はれでしょう。
はれ、雨、雨、はれ
ゆきのちくもり。
きおんは何どでしょうか。
5ど？さむいでしょう！

＊（くりかえし）

何をしていますか。
カラオケをしていますよ。
べんきょうしていますか。
ああ、そうですか。
ありがとう！サンキュー！
さあ、第七課に行きますよ！
（さあ、今！）

＊（くりかえし）

## 第八課

やきゅうを見ましたか。
はい、はい。見ましたよ！
ストライクワン、ストライクツー
ファイト！ファイト！ホームラン！
やきゅうを見ましたか。
はい、はい。行きましょう。

＊（くりかえし）

きのう、何をしましたか。
きのうですか。そうですね。
CDをきいて、べんきょうして
12時にねました。
ありがとう！サンキュー！
さあ、第八課に行きますよ！
（さあ、今！）

＊（くりかえし）

▼ Numbers

一 二 三 四 五 六

七 八 九 十 百

▼ Time

日

月 火 水 木 金 土

曜 年 今 時 分 半

前 々

▼ Parts of the body

目 口 耳 手

▼ Places and things

山 川 田 町 円

▼ ?

何

▼ Weather

天 気 雨

▼ People

父 母 子

女 男 人 友

▼ School life

学 校

本 英 語 好

▼ Adjectives

大 小

▼ Verbs

行 見 生 住 食 会